Blackmail was the only word to describe
the way the tyranical Alex Nicolaos had
forced Samantha into marrying him, but
there had been no way she could avoid
it. And certainly, physically, she realised
that he could make her respond to him.
But how could they build a marriage
when real love was so obviously lacking?

DARK
TYRANT

BY

HELEN BIANCHIN

MILLS & BOON LIMITED
15–16 BROOK'S MEWS
LONDON W1A 1DR

First published 1984
Australian copyright 1984
Philippine copyright 1984
This edition 1984

© Helen Bianchin 1984

ISBN 0 263 74791 3

Set in Monophoto Times 11 on 11 pt.
01–1084 – 47311

Made and printed in Great Britain by
Richard Clay (The Chaucer Press) Ltd,
Bungay, Suffolk

CHAPTER ONE

SAMANTHA gazed pensively out the window, marvelling that the scene beyond the expanse of plate-glass looked exactly the same as it had ten minutes ago when she'd first walked into this elegantly furnished office.

She had been nervous and vaguely curious about a letter received the previous day requesting her to phone for an appointment with the head partner of the legal firm representing her late father.

Stepfather, she corrected idly, vividly aware for the first time in years of the subtle distinction.

Her eyes were remarkably clear as she turned to meet the lawyer's carefully-assembled features. Compassion, regret, sympathy. It was as well none of these were too much in evidence, otherwise she might have let slip the tenuous hold she had on her fragile emotions.

'Why have you been empowered to enlighten me as to Dominic's finances—or lack of them, should I say?'

He cleared his throat, then spread his hands with expressive detachment. 'I understand Mr Nicolaos preferred the news be relayed by a legal representative.'

'Why?' she demanded boldly. 'Just *who* is Mr Nicolaos, and where does he feature in this deplorable mess?'

'I understand your stepfather owed Mr Nicolaos a substantial amount of money,' he revealed pragmatically. 'Those were the facts presented to me.'

Facts. One by one, they clicked through her brain like slides through a projector, inanimate and strangely alien. Dominic Roussos, father figure in her life for the past fifteen years; her mother's death seven years ago; Sophie, Dominic's sister, who had moved into the small house in suburban Perth to care for them; college, and latterly university where she was studying marine biology; Dominic's sudden death from a massive heart attack only three weeks ago.

'Are there any further questions, Miss Evans?'

Obviously he was impatient to be rid of her, and Samantha stood to her feet, thanked him with polite civility, then turned and walked towards the door.

There were so many questions burning to be answered, and they echoed inside her head as she rode the elevator down to the ground floor.

It was almost five o'clock, and the city streets were choked with traffic. She joined the queue at a nearby bus stop, and boarded the next northbound vehicle that pulled into the kerb. It meant a longer walk than usual, but she couldn't face waiting a further twenty minutes for her designated bus to arrive.

Samantha was totally immune to the soft flickering tracery of street lights that lit the city's suburbs as darkness overtook dusk in the midst of winter-cool temperatures. On alighting, she pulled the edges of her coat together and thrust her hands into the deep capacious pockets, then she set out briskly along the wide tree-lined street that ultimately joined with her own, almost a kilometre ahead.

The small brick house with its low fence and neat garden borders was a welcome sight, as was the glowing porch light over the front door.

'Samantha, you're home!'

She looked at Sophie's kindly, faintly anxious features and couldn't find it in her heart to summon any of her former anger.

'I don't need to tell you what it was all about, do I?' she slanted wryly as she shrugged off her coat and folded it over the kitchen chair.

Sophie appeared torn between conscience and loyalty. 'Things began going bad for Dominic after your mother died,' she said at last, sinking down into a nearby chair. 'I think he, too, began to slowly die. He loved her so much,' she assured Samantha earnestly, and Samantha nodded in silent agreement. 'He had a run of bad luck, light prawn catches, a series of big maintenance bills for the trawler. So he borrowed money. Then more, to pay back what he'd borrowed,' she enlightened with an expressive shrug. 'It became a vicious circle.'

'I should have been told,' Samantha said quietly, and Sophie gestured in eloquent negation. 'What could you have done?'

'Left school and got a job—anything,' declared Samantha vehemently.

'Your education was important,' Sophie protested. 'Dominic wanted you to have everything possible.'

'I would have understood,' Samantha cried, and to her great distress tears welled and began to slide slowly down her cheeks.

'Oh, sweetheart, *don't*!' begged Sophie, drawing the girl's slight figure towards her.

'It's just delayed shock, I guess,' Samantha muttered in a voice husky with emotion.

Taking a deep breath, the older woman began gently, 'I think it would be a good idea if we had a holiday. Just a week. What do you say? You have a semester break due to start on Friday, and we could go to Sydney.'

'But that's thousands of kilometres away,' Samantha protested, and glimpsed Sophie's slight smile.

'I have a sister there, nephews, nieces. It would be lovely to see them.'

The thought of new surroundings seemed ideal, if only for a short time. 'Can we afford it?'

'I have some money put aside,' Sophie revealed. 'In fact, I've already made a tentative booking with Ansett for Saturday. I'll confirm it, shall I?'

It seemed incredible that just four days later they were soaring the skies in a giant Boeing jet bound for the eastern State of New South Wales. Samantha was unable to still a natural sense of pleasure at the thought of exploring Australia's largest city, and she viewed the sprawling metropolis as the plane made a sweeping turn and began its descent.

The harbour lay beneath them, its sparkling waters spanned by impressively structured steel, and to the left could be seen the awe-inspiring majesty of the Opera House.

On clearing their luggage, they emerged from the terminal and slipped into one of several taxis lining the rank, and Samantha was too intrigued with the scenery to take much notice of the address Sophie gave the driver.

The dinginess of old terraced houses and brick walls alive with graffiti soon gave way to established elegance as gracious well-kept homes vied for supremacy with modern architecturally designed residences set amidst immaculate landscaping.

A faint prickle of unease manifested itself as the taxi turned into a wide sweeping driveway and drew to a halt outside the entrance to what could only be described as a mansion. The view across the harbour was nothing less than magnificent, and it needed scant knowledge of real estate to realise this was a very prestigious suburb.

'Sophie——'

'Be a darling and take this for me while I fix up the fare,' Sophie bade, passing over a large capacious holdall, and Samantha slid out from her seat to stand a trifle hesitantly beside the vehicle as Sophie despatched money and waited for change.

Just as she emerged, the front door opened and Samantha's attention was taken by a correctly-attired man of middle years hurrying out to greet them.

'You must be Samantha.' His smile was polite, with a touch of reserve that seemed strangely out of place. 'I'll take care of the luggage. Do please come inside.'

She was aware that Sophie had joined her, and she cast an enquiring glance, expecting an introduction. None was forthcoming, and she had little option but to enter the entrance foyer at Sophie's side.

'I'll take you directly to your rooms,' the man told them, making for a wide staircase curving towards an upper floor. 'I'm sure you'd both like to freshen up after your flight.'

From the slight deference afforded them, one could almost imagine him to be a servant, but inherent good manners forbade an enquiry until they were alone.

Samantha was shown into a luxuriously furnished suite, and she allowed her gaze to sweep over the beautifully co-ordinated tonings in silent admiration. The deep-piled carpet sank beneath her feet, its honey-cream texture a perfect foil for

the various shades of apricot utilised in the quilted
bedcover, the curtains, and the towels in the
adjoining bathroom.

She unpacked only the bare necessities, ran a
brush through her long sable-brown hair, freshened
her make-up, then made her way to Sophie's suite
across the hall.

A tentative tap on the panelled door brought a
muffled response, and Samantha turned the knob.

'Ah, there you are,' declared Sophie with a faint
smile. 'Dinner is at eight, I believe. Spiros is
expecting us downstairs for drinks.'

'Your brother-in-law?'

'No.'

Samantha's direct gaze narrowed fractionally.
'Who is he?'

'Spiros?' Sophie's mouth curved warmly, although her voice seemed deliberately bland. 'A
friend. Now, shall we have that drink? I could do
with one.' Moving forward, she tucked her hand
beneath Samantha's elbow and led the way out
into the hall.

'He doesn't own this house.' It was a statement
rather than a question, and when Sophie didn't
comment, Samantha queried, 'Who does? Some
millionaire acquaintance?'

They reached the bottom of the stairs, and she
sensed the slight tension apparent as Sophie
gestured towards a door to their left.

'Why are you being so evasive?' she demanded
quietly, and received no reply as the older woman
directed her into an elegantly furnished lounge.
'Sophie?' Her voice held a hint of exasperation
which was smoothly ignored.

'Good evening.'

Samantha glanced up at the sound of the deep,
faintly-inflected drawl, and her eyes flew wide as

they settled on a tall well-built man standing on the far side of the room.

Dynamic and infinitely masculine, he projected a raw virility that was electrifying. Expert tailoring lent sophisticated civility, and did little to tame the sheer animal magnetism of the man. In his late thirties, he bore the air of supreme wealth with careless ease. Someone it would be infinitely wiser to have as a friend than an enemy, she thought with a faint shiver.

'You had a pleasant flight, I trust?'

Who was he? Some deep-rooted instinct screamed an angry rejection even as Sophie conducted the necessary introduction.

'Samantha, you haven't met Alex, have you?'

Alex. *Alex Nicolaos*. It could only be him. But *why*? She turned blindly towards Sophie, silently demanding an explanation, and glimpsed the faint tinge of colour in the older woman's cheeks.

'We are here as Alex's guests——'

'At my suggestion,' he intervened smoothly, crossing the room to pause within touching distance.

The faint musky tang of his aftershave teased her nostrils, and for some reason his closeness affected her breathing, heightening an awareness she found vaguely frightening.

'Your father was an old family friend,' Alex declared quietly. 'It saddened me to learn of his passing.'

Her nerves felt on edge and as taut as a tightly-stretched piece of wire. What could she say? Thank him for extending his hospitality?

There was a hard ruthlessness beneath the surface that was oddly at variance with the expressed sympathy of his words, and despite the warmth within the room, a chill shiver feathered its way down her spine.

'What will you have to drink?' he enquired smoothly, and she dimly heard Sophie request a brandy and soda. 'Samantha?'

She needed something alcoholic to steady her nerves, yet on an empty stomach she hesitated to opt for spirits. 'A small glass of white wine.'

'Sweet or dry?'

She said the first thing that came into her head. 'Riesling if you have it.' The thought that he might not almost brought a bubble of hysterical laughter to her lips. If she'd requested Dom Perignon he would undoubtedly reach into his well-stocked bar-fridge and produce a chilled bottle.

Samantha watched as he crossed to a cabinet and began pouring drinks, then when he returned she accepted a glass from his outstretched hand with untold care.

There wasn't one solitary experience she could draw from that would offer suitable panache with which to deal with a man of Alex Nicolaos' calibre. He was light years ahead of her, sophisticated to an alarming degree, and she fervently wished she was anywhere but here.

'Your rooms are to your liking?'

She raised startled eyes at the sound of that smooth drawl and effected a polite response.

'Beautiful, Alex,' added Sophie in assurance. 'The view across the harbour must be unsurpassed.'

'The very reason which prompted me to buy the house,' he revealed, lifting the glass to his lips.

Samantha watched with mesmerised fascination as he took a long swallow, and she caught sight of the strong muscled column of his throat, its dark-tanned skin shown in stark contrast against the snowy whiteness of his shirt linen.

She must be going mad, she decided, attempting

to pull her emotions together, and following his actions, she took an appreciative sip of wine.

There were several oil paintings gracing the walls and she let her gaze wander over each in turn. Her knowledge was fairly limited, but unless she was mistaken, one resembled a Renoir, another an equally revered Master. If he was a collector, he had impeccable taste.

'You admire works of art?'

'Doesn't everyone?' she parried, forcing herself to meet his studied gaze.

'Yet the science of Art was not included in your scholastic curriculum.'

How could he know that? 'Certain subjects form part of the mainstream course,' she explained politely. 'Outside of these, the choice is limited. It's a matter of priorities.'

'You enjoy varsity life?'

What was the reason for his interest? 'The lectures, or the general student bonhomie?'

'Samantha is a dedicated student,' this from Sophie, who knew better than anyone precisely how many hours were spent in study.

'I'm sure you have something of more interest to discuss,' Samantha found herself saying, and saw a faint gleam of amusement in those dark eyes.

At that moment Spiros appeared and announced dinner, and Alex led them towards a formal dining room where an elaborately set table reposed in magnificent splendour. With considerable ease he indicated where they should sit, and held out each chair in turn before taking his position at the head of the table.

Where else? Samantha decided wryly, aware of a warm tingling sensation down the length of her back where his fingers had lightly brushed only seconds before as he had pushed in her chair. She

felt inexplicably cross at her reaction, at odds with
sensations she had not previously experienced.
Loath to explore them too deeply, she came to the
seemingly logical conclusion that recent shock was
responsible for her vulnerability.

The meal comprised no less than five courses,
each separate one a perfection in its own right,
so that at the conclusion Samantha could only
echo Sophie's appreciation and follow Alex's
direction that they partake coffee in the lounge.
Conversation had been surprisingly fluid, and after
the initial starter she had begun to relax, entering
into the discourse without being aware of it—due
largely to her host's skilled adroitness, she
suspected, and the effect good wine had in
loosening her tongue.

'May I suggest a tour of the city and suburbs
tomorrow?'

Samantha accepted coffee from the hovering
Spiros, refused the addition of spirit, but accepted
sugar and cream.

'That would be delightful,' Sophie agreed,
turning slightly towards Samantha. 'Don't you
agree?'

'You're very kind, Mr Nicolaos,' she murmured
dutifully, not quite meeting his gaze.

'You must call me Alex,' he drawled.

Must she? It seemed a liberty she felt unsure she
should take, instinct warning that to become
personally involved, even to the slightest degree,
harboured infinite danger.

'You have not previously been to Sydney, I
believe?'

'No.' The wine was beginning to make her feel
sleepy—that, and the effects of air travel. Jet-lag,
she corrected.

'There are several places of interest,' Alex

continued, his expression deliberately enigmatic. 'Through the week my car, with Spiros at the wheel, will be at your disposal.'

'Thank you.' God, she decided wearily, she sounded like a polite little schoolgirl. Without thought she stood to her feet and placed her cup down on to a nearby table. 'If you'll both excuse me?' She glanced towards Sophie. 'I'm very tired.' It wasn't just an excuse. 'Goodnight.' Her gaze skimmed towards Alex, then without a further word she crossed the room and made her way upstairs.

Closing the door of her suite, she moved to the bathroom and ran water into the capacious tub, added essence from one of several bottles provided, then she went back to the bedroom, noticing at once the coverlet had been removed and her nightgown lay neatly folded on the pillow.

A quick glance revealed that her clothes had been unpacked and now reposed neatly on hangers and in drawers.

Such untold luxury was unknown, and she pondered a trifle wryly that a week of being cosseted would be nice, although given a choice, she would opt for her host being other than Alex Nicolaos.

The hot scented water had a soothing effect, and she soaked unrepentantly until tiredness dictated she emerge. Towelled dry, she donned her nightgown and slipped between silken sheets, to drift within minutes into blissful somnolence.

CHAPTER TWO

SAMANTHA woke to the sound of curtains being opened, and for a moment she felt disorientated by her surroundings, until memory surfaced.

'Good morning,' a slightly accented voice greeted her with startling joviality. 'I am Serafina, wife of Spiros, and I have brought your breakfast.'

Indeed, there was a laden tray in her hands, and Samantha scrambled into a sitting position, pulling a spare pillow behind her to provide a satisfactory backrest. The aroma of freshly-brewed coffee tantalised her tastebuds, and intermingled with devilled kidneys and bacon, a light fluffy omelette, croissants and strawberry conserve, it looked a breakfast fit for royalty.

'There's more food here than I normally eat in a whole day,' she protested with a slight smile, and incurred Serafina's admonishing headshake.

'Breakfast is an important meal. A good start, yes?' Her sparkling eyes skimmed Samantha's delicate features. 'You are too thin, you must eat.'

She was slim, it was true, but thin? Her gently-curved figure reflected a pleasing outline whenever she viewed its overall effect in the mirror. Of average height, she possessed long nicely-shaped legs, small hips, a slender waist, and nicely-proportioned breasts. Ballet practice lent a natural grace, and while her facial structure wasn't startling, her skin was clear, and her eyes were a deep tawny-gold—luminous and expressive, an ardent male admirer had once extolled.

'I'll do my best,' Samantha promised, noting the neatly-folded newspaper Serafina placed on the bed. Alex Nicolaos certainly believed in spoiling his guests!

'There is no hurry. Please take your time.'

Well, why not enjoy such luxury while she could? Sunday was obviously regarded as a day of leisure, and it wasn't until Serafina had left the room that Samantha remembered their host's indication that a sightseeing tour was on the day's agenda.

It was almost nine when she emerged from her room. She had elected to wear slim-fitting brush-denim trousers and a lambswool jumper, for the weather looked bleak with the promise of rain. Dress jeans were both fashionable and warm, strictly wash-and-wear, and precluded the use of pantyhose in winter—a necessary saving on her student allowance.

A light tap on Sophie's door brought no response, and concluding that she had already gone downstairs, Samantha made her way to the lower floor.

Unsure precisely where to look, she hovered uncertainly at the foot of the stairs, and almost jumped with fright as a deep voice sounded immediately behind her.

'Good morning.'

She turned at once, a hesitant smile tugging the edge of her lips as she returned the greeting. 'Where is everyone, Spiros?'

'I believe Mr Nicolaos is in the study.'

'And Sophie?'

'She rose early.'

Very illuminating, she thought wryly. It scarcely explained anything, and she was on the verge of enquiring precisely as to Sophie's whereabouts

when a door opened opposite the lounge to reveal
Alex Nicolaos in its aperture.

Attired in slim-fitting dark trousers, a leather
jacket left open, and his shirt carelessly unbuttoned
at the neck, he bore an air of casual elegance that
was a marked contrast to the formal business suit
he had worn the previous evening.

'Ah, there you are,' he greeted her lazily. 'I trust
you slept well?'

So much solicitude over her welfare! 'How could
I not?' she responded lightly, aware that Spiros
was no longer sharing their company. 'Where is
Sophie?'

'Serafina has just deposited a large pot of coffee
in my study. Come and join me. We can talk
there.'

Talk? About what, for heaven's sake? She didn't
particularly want to be alone with him, and the
prospect of being closeted in his study caused
alarm to spiral through her body. Yet if she
refused, it would seem churlish. 'Thank you.'

Her pulse seemed to quicken in beat as he stood
aside for her to precede him, and once inside the
large room she gave a start as the door shut with a
soft thud. For some reason it had an ominous
sound. She was being fanciful, allowing a vivid
imagination to take hold without any logical
motive, she dismissed uneasily.

'Sugar, and a dash of cream, I believe?'

Samantha glanced towards the wide, tradi-
tionally-crafted credenza where he stood poised in
the act of dispensing coffee from a well-laden tray.

'Thank you.' She was beginning to respond
parrot-fashion, she thought with a touch of
hysteria. Yet why did she feel as if she was
standing on the edge of a precipice? It was crazy!

Her eyes wandered over the masculine room,

noting the leather chairs, and an impressive desk. Bookshelves lined one wall floor to ceiling, and a large brick fireplace was a focal point directly opposite. Not merely decorative, for logs burned in its grate, the flames flickering softly, giving out a welcome warmth.

'Sit down, Samantha.'

She just stopped herself from voicing words of thanks for the third time and sank into the nearest chair. Accepting a cup and saucer from his hand, she watched as he moved towards the large desk and leaned against its edge.

His regard seemed deliberately enigmatic, and it took all her courage not to rise to her feet and flee the room. His strong features assumed a solemnity she found frightening, and there was nothing to be gained from his expression.

'I ensured you were aware of certain facts before you left Perth,' Alex drawled a trifle brusquely, shooting her a dark glance. 'I see no reason not to relay those remaining.'

'You're scaring me.' The words were out before she could halt them. She felt incredibly vulnerable, and all her preconceived doubts rose to the surface as she held his gaze. 'Shouldn't Sophie be here as well?'

'Sophie is aware of all the facts.'

'I see,' Samantha said slowly. 'I find it hard to believe I was brought all this way simply to be given them in person.'

'Dominic was deeply in debt. So deep,' he elaborated dryly, 'that he resorted to borrowing money from unethical sources. When he failed to deliver on time, they exhorted a higher interest, demanded more security, until there was nothing left.'

His eyes never left her face, and she felt

mesmerised, like a defenceless victim awaiting the strike of a deadly snake.

'Three years ago he bartered for more time, more money, with his only remaining asset,' he continued, adding with quiet emphasis, 'You.'

None of this was true, she thought wildly. He was making it up—he had to be!

'Sixteen, and even then startlingly beautiful, you were presented as a virginal prize to the highest bidder. The conditions were few. Your education was to be maintained for the next three years, an allowance granted to cover clothing and sundry expenses, the house you lived in with Sophie to be available until you completed your studies.'

Samantha looked at him with growing horror, refusing to believe what he said. Her face felt drained of colour, and her eyes seemed huge with incredulity and pain.

'To give Dominic his due, he had no inkling of a lapse into ill-health, or his inability to eventually discharge his liabilities.'

There was silence, a space of time that seemed suspended as she fought to retain some sort of normalcy in what was the most bizarre situation she had ever imagined.

'Are you trying to say you *own* me?'

He regarded her with an unwavering scrutiny, then answered with stark cynicism, 'Yes.'

She lifted her head, and her eyes sparkled with angry tears. 'How do you propose I tender repayment? Or shouldn't I be that naïve?' she demanded scornfully, and saw one eyebrow slant in sardonic mockery.

'I imagine I have succeeded in shattering every fond memory you retain of your stepfather. He did, however, redeem himself to some small degree by making one stipulation in the event he was unable to fulfil his financial obligations.'

'I'm almost afraid to ask,' said Samantha.

'Marriage.'

The word fell with all the force of a megaton bomb, and she rounded on him with total antipathy. 'Do you expect me to believe any of this?'

A muscle tensed along his jaw, making his features seem infinitely formidable. 'You want proof?'

'Yes—*yes*, damn you!'

Without a word he crossed round behind the desk, opened a drawer and extracted papers, then silently placed them into her grasp.

Her hands shook as she forced herself to read the typewritten text, and she experienced a growing sense of horror that everything Alex Nicolaos had told her was nothing less than the truth.

'How could he?' she asked in shocked disbelief, and his eyes hardened until they resembled polished ebony.

'Be grateful Dominic approached me privately before putting such a contract on the open market.'

Samantha gazed at him with utter loathing. 'Honour among thieves, you mean?'

'I paid off all his debts, took over the title deeds to the house in Perth, backed his trawling ventures when the catches failed to meet expenses,' he revealed sardonically. 'Tuition fees—education, ballet, the extra coaching you received, sporting clubs. Clothes, the small matter of an allowance— even the food you ate.'

'And now it's time to collect.' She said it dully, almost without thought. She had surpassed anger, and was now in a numbed state of limbo. 'Why *marriage*?'

'Dominic insisted I take care of you, and I gave him my word,' he said wryly.

'Noble of you!'

'Considering the amount involved,' he declared dryly. 'It was.'

'And what was Sophie's part in this diabolical scheme?' She gave a hollow laugh. 'Or is it stupid of me to even ask?' she mocked in self-derision. 'She was enlisted to deliver the goods—*me*.' Her eyes swept over him. 'No wonder she didn't answer when I knocked on her door earlier! I suppose she's been paid, and gone.'

'Sophie is visiting her sister on the northern side of the city. Spiros drove her there early this morning.'

'No doubt before Serafina even woke me with breakfast.'

His silence was answer enough, and Samantha stood to her feet. 'I'm not to be informed as to her whereabouts. Nor, I imagine, is she supposed to contact me. Oh, you've been very clever, Mr Nicolaos. But not quite clever enough.' She was shaking with pent-up fury. 'That—so-called contract may have some meaning to you, but I doubt the legal fraternity would view it with any favour.'

'That's debatable,' he allowed silkily. 'However, be sure of one pertinent fact. As Dominic's sole beneficiary, *you* are now responsible for the debts of his estate.'

She felt a mounting sense of panic as figures raced through her brain with blinding confusion. She was unsure of the total, but it could nevertheless be counted in hundreds of thousands, rather than mere thousands—operative expenses for an ongoing fleet of trawlers were considerable.

God! There was no way she could pay back that sort of money in a lifetime.

'I could have the estate declared bankrupt,' she declared as the thought occurred.

'So you could,' Alex agreed with remote detachment. 'But be aware of the repercussions such an action would have. Not only would you be compelled to pay a proportion meted out by the court of all future earnings, you would be unable to gain assistance from any financial institution. The slur bankruptcy carries would also affect any career opportunities.'

He had her backed into a corner, and it rankled. 'You paid a very high price,' she flung with unaccustomed asperity. 'What if you've purchased second-hand goods?'

His smile made her stomach tighten with fear. 'It isn't your virginity I want,' he dismissed with cruel inflexibility. 'Your youthful body in my bed to use whenever I feel the need, to receive my seed and bear my children—sons, if the good gods are willing.' His eyes raked her slender frame with pitiless disregard. 'Marriage is a convenient solution, for both of us.'

'I don't consider it convenient for *me*,' Samantha retorted with utter loathing, her eyes alive with golden fire as she stood there in utter defiance. 'There's nothing in this world that would make me agree to such blatant blackmail!' She had to get out of the room and away from him, and she moved towards the door.

'You refuse?'

At that silky query she paused and turned slightly to face him. 'I'd rather go to Hell first,' she denounced with conviction. He was a ruthless, calculating *bastard*!

'Indeed?' One eyebrow slanted with mocking

cynicism. 'What do you intend now? To flee as far and as fast as your slim legs will carry you?'

'You can't keep me a prisoner,' she declared decisively, aware even in anger of his watchful stance.

'Lack of money is a restriction in itself,' drawled Alex with merciless finality. 'Without it, you can't go far.'

It was the last straw to be loaded on the proverbial camel's back. He had covered all the angles, and he knew it. Yet still she refused to give in. 'My allowance is terminated, I gather?' The few notes and coins she had in her purse would cover the bus fare into the city, and perhaps buy food for a day or two, but it wouldn't pay for even the most frugal of lodgings. As to a bank account, she didn't possess one. Everything from the clothes she wore to pocket money, had been handed out by Sophie or Dominic. The thought of accepting charity was galling, but she was willing to grasp at anything in an effort to break free of Alex Nicolaos.

'The nearest Social Welfare office won't be unsympathetic. I can claim unemployment benefit.'

'The wheels of bureaucracy turn very slowly. How do you propose to survive until the first payment is granted?'

'There must be something I can do,' she said tightly, and a hollow laugh escaped her lips. 'The oldest game in the book requires no qualifications.'

In seeming slow motion she watched as he moved away from the desk and began walking towards her.

'A lady of the night?' he queried silkily, coming to a halt mere inches away.

Samantha's heart began to pound with a mixture of fear and damning awareness. Every sensory nerve-end seemed to pulse with vibrant life, throwing her equilibrium into chaotic confusion.

'Do you imagine the men will all be young, or even acceptable?' His eyes held sardonic cynicism. 'Those who enlist the services of a prostitute expect to get what they pay for, and the higher the price, the prettier the trick to be performed.'

Samantha felt sickened by the vision his words evoked, yet pride forced her to retort, 'What you're advocating isn't so very different. Either I sell my body to one man—or several.' The thought of him in the role of lover unfurled a multitude of sensations she was loath to explore. 'Somehow I think I'd rather stand in front of an oncoming bus,' she declared trenchantly.

'Rather drastic, don't you think?'

'Not if I died.' Her lips trembled slightly. 'At least then I'd escape everything—especially *you*!'

'Only a foolish innocent would fail to distinguish between the two,' he said brusquely.

Samantha lifted her chin and regarded him with bitter enmity. 'Am I supposed to be flattered, even grateful, you've offered marriage?'

'Then you agree?'

'*No*, damn you!'

His eyes narrowed, and his features became an expressionless mask. 'In that case,' he drawled, 'I will buy a few hours of your time.' His eyes raked over her slight frame with analytical thoroughness. 'At'—he paused with deliberate insolence—'fifty dollars an hour.'

'How much?' she gasped with incredulity, and saw his mouth twist with mocking disparagement.

'You'll earn it, my dear. For that fee, I shall insist on some high-class action.'

Every nerve in her body shrieked with shock at his words, and her vocal chords appeared to have lapsed into temporary paralysis.

'Starting now,' Alex insisted with deadly calm.

'Here?' She had no recollection of voicing that high monosyllabic query.

'Why not?' His eyes never left her face. 'The fire will provide adequate warmth.'

Her gaze slid to the impeccable bearskin on the floor, and couldn't imagine anything more decadent than taking part in copulation there—or anywhere, for that matter. She wildly refused to call it *lovemaking*.

Slowly, and with deliberate movements, he shrugged off his jacket.

Mesmerised fascination held her rooted to the spot as he unbuttoned his shirt, and when his hands went to unfasten his belt, returning sanity made escape imperative. Without thought she turned and ran, only to be brought to a sudden halt as hard hands caught hold of her arms.

'Let me go!'

His dark eyes became icily remote. 'So shy?'

Samantha hated the easy strength with which he held her, and she began to struggle in earnest as he drew her close. So close she was made aware of every tautened muscle and sinew. 'Don't touch me!'

'You won't get very far if you advocate the "hands off" technique.' His smile was without humour. 'It will only incite your—clientele to be justifiably and perhaps indelicately brutal.'

Panic-stricken, she aimed her foot at his shin, becoming exultant when she connected, then she cried out with sudden pain as his hold tightened into bands of steel.

'What if someone comes in? Spiros—

Serafina——' She was jabbering, her breath coming in short sharp gasps as she struggled to break free of him.

'Either will knock first, then wait until summoned before entering. In any case, the house is mine,' he drawled with arrogant assurance. 'To do as I want, with whoever I choose.' His grip altered as he caught first one hand, then the other behind her back, and she was powerless to evade that dark descending head.

His mouth fastened with unerring accuracy over hers, forcing apart her tightly-closed lips with ruthless brutality, and a silent moan died in her throat as he began a ravaging exploration that annihilated every conception of what a kiss was meant to be.

It went on, and on, until it became a savage possession that allowed and gave no quarter. Her neck ached, as did her jaw, and she tasted blood as the soft inner tissue split and became grazed. Then mercifully her mouth was relinquished, and she drew in great gulps of air in an effort to regain her breath.

A cry of outrage emerged scant seconds later as his lips trailed down to settle over the slight hollows at the base of her throat, then slipped lower, following the vee of her jumper.

Not content, his hands slid to her waist, and in one swift movement the restricting garment was pulled over her head and tossed to the floor.

With clinical detachment he sought the softness of her breasts, dispensing with the thin scrap of silk and lace with accomplished ease.

His fingers brushed across the vulnerable peaks, then slid lower to cup each breast, the movement strangely evocative.

'Don't!' Her voice was a scandalised whisper,

and she almost died at the expression in those dark eyes as they met her own.

'Are you begging?'

Oh, God. What had she done to deserve this? A long shudder raked her slim form as his fingers trailed across each peak in turn, then began a tantalising caress until they burgeoned with pulsating life beneath his touch.

She was shocked into speechlessness when his head descended and his mouth closed over one vulnerable peak. Sensations she never knew existed spiralled from the central core of her being, radiating through her body until she groaned with despair. As his lips slid towards its twin and began a similar onslaught she cried out for him to desist, then resorted to an impassioned moan as her pleas went unheeded.

She wanted to cry, to rage against him, and when she thought she could stand no more she brought her face down to his, seeking anything with her teeth in an effort to get him to stop.

His swift intake of breath was the only satisfaction she gained as she caught hold of an earlobe and bit hard, then she screamed as an excruciating pain shot like a knife through her breast.

The sound was effectively silenced as his mouth closed over hers, and if she had thought his previous assault was a plundering punishment, this was nothing short of violation.

When his hands sought the fastening of her jeans she went curiously still. The liberties he was capable of taking, the sure knowledge that he *would*, brought a single negation to her lips.

'No?' Alex queried cynically, his eyes strangely watchful.

Samantha felt devoid of all emotion, drained, and curiously detached. 'You've made your point.'

'Indeed?'

Slowly she lifted her head and met the savage ruthlessness evident in his implacable features. 'That was what the entire exercise was about, wasn't it?' If only she could curl up and die; anything would be better than having to stand here and eat humble pie. Yet the alternative was worse—he had very effectively proved that.

'Perhaps,' he allowed cryptically, and she was temporarily robbed of speech by his admission.

'The odds are strongly in your favour,' Samantha managed tonelessly, hugging her arms across her breasts. 'Three square meals a day, a more than adequate roof over my head.' A hollow laugh emerged from her throat, tinged with self-mockery. 'If I have to sell myself, I may as well do it in luxurious comfort.'

'You seem to have forgotten one pertinent fact. Your—services have already been paid for.'

She felt close to hysteria. 'Silk—or do you prefer satin, sheets on the bed?' Hatred made her taunt, 'I trust you're an experienced tutor.'

'Do you doubt it?'

A shudder racked her slender frame. His expertise had been startlingly apparent, even when tinged with cruelty.

'Now that my lesson in humiliation is over, you won't object if I get dressed?' Her attempt at cool anger failed dismally in the face of his mocking cynicism.

'My dear, your attributes are infinitely pleasing. It seems almost a shame to cover them.'

Colour flooded her cheeks, and she bent down to retrieve her clothes, then she slipped them on with more haste than care. 'I hope your taste doesn't run to nude titillation, because I refuse to comply.'

sss

'You are scarcely in a position to refuse me anything.'

Unbidden, her hand snaked towards his face, the small explosion of sound seeming loud in the silence of the room. The mark on his cheek was white on his tanned skin, then before her horrified gaze it slowly darkened to a dull red.

'Little fool,' Alex muttered with dangerous softness, and reaching out he caught her hands in a bone-crushing grip. His eyes gleamed with glittery anger, and he looked furious enough to strike her. 'I could take you now, here, and no one would stop me.'

'But you won't.' Conviction leant her voice surprising strength. 'Like a sadistic jungle animal you'll play me out until it's time for the kill.' Her eyes flashed with bitterness. 'Just be sure how much I hate you, and with each day that passes, I'll hate you more!'

He reached out a hand and let his fingers rest on the rapidly-beating pulse at the base of her throat. 'You may hate me with your brain, but this,' he tapped the offending spot with feather lightness, 'tells me your body is not immune to my touch.' His lips curved into a sardonic smile. 'Hate me as much as you want, Samantha.'

With unhurried movements he buttoned his shirt, then shrugged into his jacket. The look he cast her was curiously detached as he crossed towards the desk.

'You've hardly touched your coffee,' he said dispassionately, and she experienced a wild desire to laugh.

'Oh, by all means let's sit down over fresh coffee,' she derided. 'Business has been completed, and now it's time to observe the conventions.'

'Not quite.'

'You mean there's more?'

'We have a wedding to arrange,' Alex drawled. 'Or had you forgotten?'

Her eyes flashed with bitter enmity as they met his. 'I'm surprised you intend to consult me.'

'I already have the necessary licence,' he informed her silkily, and she rounded on him in fury.

'You egotistical bastard! You were so damned sure of me?'

His hard, rough-chiselled features became stern and uncompromising. 'Sarcasm doesn't suit you.'

'At the moment it appears to be my only weapon,' Samantha returned waspishly.

'Coffee,' he said abruptly. 'With a dash of brandy to steady your nerves.' His intent gaze brooked no refusal. 'I insist.'

'Insist as much as you like,' she retorted, uncaring of the dark inimical anger apparent. 'And there's nothing wrong with my nerves!'

His appraisal was swift and hatefully analytical as he raked her slim form. 'In that case, we'll leave.'

Her eyes widened with perplexity. 'Leave?'

'I offered to act as guide, remember?' Alex prompted cynically.

The sightseeing tour. How could she have forgotten? The thought of sitting beside him for a number of hours as he drove through the city and suburbs made her feel ill. 'I don't think I could bear it.'

'Yes,' he responded with quiet insistence. 'Serafina has already packed some picnic fare, and she will be disappointed if we change our plans.'

She rounded on him, quivering with fury. 'I'd rather be alone.' Suddenly it was all too much. 'Damn you, Alex Nicolaos! The whole lot of you—Sophie, *Dominic*. I wish I'd never heard of any of you!'

'One cannot change the past.'

'No,' she agreed stormily. 'But I should be permitted to have a say in my future.'

'What will be so very different?'

'You can't mean that!'

'Eventually you would marry. I am not averse to you continuing with your ballet tuition, if it is important to you. As to a career—it no longer is necessary for you to earn a living.'

'I love dancing!' It was a cry from the heart, and he leaned back against the side of the desk, his eyes darkly inscrutable.

'There is a studio in the basement, complete with sauna and spa. I use it to work out.' He effected a careless shrug. 'The previous owner was a fitness enthusiast. Feel free to avail yourself of it at any time.'

It wasn't the competitiveness of dancing she enjoyed, or the plaudits to be earned. Rather the fluidity of style, which with disciplined exercise meant she could direct her body and limbs to express an extension of the music. Classical, modern; nothing was exempt. She could listen for hours, letting the orchestration flow through to her very soul until it became alive within her, taking charge. Then she would dance, preferably alone, and that feeling of oneness with the music became an exhilaration of body and spirit.

'What about my studies?' she queried.

'I doubt if a degree in marine biology will be useful,' Alex drawled cynically, and she retaliated with matching cynicism.

'Spoke like a true chauvinist! A woman has no place in a man's domain.'

'I imagine the study of marine life has several

women exponents who are equally, if not better qualified, than their male counterparts. I simply fail to see the necessity to complete studies that will have no part in your life.'

'What if I insist?'

He moved away from the desk and came towards her, pausing only when he was within touching distance. 'I want a full-time wife, Samantha.'

'In other words, you want me to be available expressly for your pleasure.'

His eyes gleamed with wry humour. 'That, too.'

A swift tide of colour swept over her cheeks, and she felt incredibly angry. 'There was never any doubt I'd be required to occupy your bed.'

'Shall we go?'

'I'd rather not, if you don't mind.'

'Oh, but I do.' He placed a hand beneath her elbow, and she wrenched it away.

'I'm quite capable of walking without your help!'

His eyes narrowed, and his expression became vaguely forbidding. 'Go and get a coat. It's cold outside.'

For a moment Samantha considered defying him, then she capitulated with a weary shrug. What was the use?

CHAPTER THREE

THE sleek Mercedes sports coupé purred along the road with leashed ease beneath Alex's competent hands.

He had assumed a mantle of sophisticated urbanity, almost as if their volatile exchange had not taken place, and he pointed out places of scenic interest as they drove round Vaucluse, Rose Bay, Double Bay, viewed the Royal Botanic Gardens, then strolled around the outside of the famed Opera House.

Lunch was eaten picnic-style in Hyde Park in the company of innumerable friendly pigeons who regarded every lingering passer-by as a source of food. The weak winter sunshine struggled through gathering clouds as Samantha endeavoured to do justice to the food Serafina had provided. There were crusty fresh bread rolls and soft curls of butter, pâté, enormous prawns resting in individual salad bowls, sliced chicken and thin slivers of meat in a delicate sauce. Cheese, fruit, and a bottle of excellent chilled white wine proved a palatable complement, and she refused coffee with a sigh of utter repletion.

There was a strange sense of unreality pervading the day, and she was supremely conscious of Alex Nicolaos, the man, and what he represented. She couldn't look at him without being vividly reminded of the way he had kissed her, and as for the rest of it—her skin burned where his mouth had touched, and her breasts swelled within the confines of her bra, making her aware of their tenderness with every breath she took.

If only she could have time alone in which to think! Marriage was something she had hitherto not given a great deal of thought, regarding it hazily, unsure of its priority in her immediate future. She had always been a serious student, and as an only child she had rarely relied on others for company or entertainment. Her waking hours were inevitably filled with scholastic lectures, dancing lessons, tennis, squash, swimming, and study. Socially, she kept a low profile by choice, although the invitations were many.

Perhaps if she had made time to pursue a social existence she might have felt free to indulge in sex like most of her fellow students. The stark truth was that she had yet to meet the man able to persuade her into his bed. Whether or not such moralistic principles were a rarity in this day and age was debateable. All she knew was that she wanted it to be right, to actually feel the need to gift her body; not only that, for her lover to need her as much as she needed him.

Now she was to be flung into a marriage she didn't want with a man she'd never even heard of until a week ago. What sort of life would she have as Alex Nicolaos' wife? Hardly cherished or adored! How could she live with him, physically *love* him? She had no reason to like him—every motive to hate the intolerable position in which he had placed her. A wealthy man, he wanted an heir—in all probability, more than one. What chance would such children have, brought up in an environment where their parents had little affection, let alone love, for each other?

'What is going on in that head of yours?'

Samantha glanced across to the man sitting

opposite, noting the powerful strength evident in those saturnine features, and her chin unconsciously lifted a fraction. 'Perhaps I'm plotting my escape.'

'I wouldn't advise it,' Alex warned with dangerous softness.

'No,' she conceded with undue solemnity as she met his impenetrable gaze. 'But you must know I don't want to marry you.'

'What is it that frightens you the most?' he queried with a touch of mockery. 'Me? Or the idea of marriage itself?'

'Both!'

A faint smile widened his mouth. 'Ah—honesty.'

'Nice that I amuse you!' Samantha scrambled to her feet, every line of her slim body taut with anger.

'You look like a gazelle on the verge of flight,' Alex drawled, and leaning out he captured her wrist.

'You're hurting me!'

'On the contrary, I'm being careful to ensure that I don't,' he said smoothly.

'Let me go, Alex!' Her eyes filled with shimmering tears, a futility against an invidious fate. 'You can't want *me*.'

'Now you're being fanciful.'

'Am I?' she queried sadly. 'In one short week I've had every illusion shattered. The man I loved as a father bartered me as saleable goods; aided and abetted by a woman of whom I'd become very fond. And as chief perpetrator, you not only agreed to it, you actually encouraged the duplicity. Am I supposed to condone it?'

Applying the merest pressure, he forced her to her knees on the rug, and his expression was curiously implacable. 'I was aware how desperate, even fanatical, Dominic had become in an attempt to recover his losses. If I hadn't acted when I did, you would have been fair game for any of the unscrupulous wolves who regard human bait as a diverse titillation. Some would have put you to work and recouped their investment.' His mouth twisted with wry cynicism. 'Do I need to elaborate?'

The angry thoughtless words she had carelessly flung in his face earlier about choosing to solicit in an attempt to earn her keep suddenly became horrifyingly ironic.

Alex taunted quietly, 'You'd have been on a one-way trip to Hell without being able to do a thing about it—believe me.'

'Somehow I can't regard you as a knight in shining armour,' she choked, feeling torn apart.

'Did I profess to be one?'

She couldn't look at him, and didn't demur when he stood to his feet and began repacking the remains of their lunch into the hamper.

With the movements of an automaton, she rose and caught the edges of the rug, folded it carefully, then she carried it to the car.

The splendour of the north shore suburbs and their many picturesque bays were lost as Samantha gazed sightlessly out of the window, and she was scarcely aware of the background music on the cassette-deck as the Mercedes ate up the kilometres with smooth precision.

There seemed nothing more to say, and she didn't feel inclined to enter into inane conversation simply for the sake of it.

The inner city was alive with people of all ages, providing a colourful ribbon of movement against the multitude of brightly-dressed shop windows.

Conventional architecture vied with towering structures of steel and plate-glass, a concession to space-age development.

Alex didn't stop, choosing instead to pull in beside a small colonial-style hotel in Double Bay.

'Let's go inside for a drink.'

Samantha glanced at him, then gave a slight grimace. 'I'm not exactly dressed for it.'

His eyes ran over her neatly-attired figure, and he gave a light shrug. 'You look fine.'

She wanted to cry out for him to take her home—her home. Except that humble abode was thousands of kilometres away on the other side of the continent. A faintly bitter laugh was stifled before it could emerge. She no longer had a home. In fact, she had nothing. Even the clothes she wore, probably right down to her pants and bra, had been bought and paid for by the man at her side.

'What would you like?'

Samantha looked at him blankly, then endeavoured to marshal her thoughts. The small lounge was well patronised, the hovering waiter obviously wanting to take their order and move on. 'Could I have something hot?'

'An Irish coffee, perhaps?' Alex suggested, glancing at her for verification. 'Or a Jamaican, with Tia Maria?'

That sounded much more palatable. 'Jamaican, thank you.'

'Make it two,' he advised the waiter smoothly.

There was a measurable silence, and she became consumed with awkwardness, at odds with herself and the strange inimical man sitting opposite. In a rush, she said the first words that came into her head.

'I presume you'll be in touch with Sophie?'

His gaze was startlingly direct. 'Yes. She will be anxious to hear the outcome.'

Her lips twisted wryly. 'Was there ever any doubt?'

'No.'

The waiter returned with two steaming glasses of aromatic coffee fringed with cream and laced with liqueur.

'Can I speak to her?'

Alex's expression became enigmatic. 'Of course. Over the next few days she will accompany you on a shopping expedition.'

'As a confidante, or bodyguard?' As soon as the words were out she regretted them, but it was too late to retract, and she saw his eyes narrow.

'You would be advised to accept the situation.'

Steady, she cautioned. She'd have to take hold of herself, otherwise she would only heap more retribution on her hapless head. His one chastisement to date had been pitilessly explicit, and she wasn't keen to experience another.

'What exactly is it that you do to earn a living?' Surely as his soon-to-be wife she had the right to ask.

'Question and answer time?' Alex mused cynically.

'You know everything there is to know about me,' she said simply.

'Ask away,' he mocked lightly, and she met his gaze steadily.

'I've already asked the first question.'

A slight smile curved his lips into a sensuous line. 'I buy and sell—property, shares. I'm also on the boards of several companies. I own a few racehorses.' His shoulders made a negligent shrug. 'You could say I have a finger in several ventures.'

'That's it?'

'You want more?'

'Is there any?' she queried, slightly startled.

'I take an active part in municipal affairs.'

'Politics?'

'No.' His dark eyes appeared to sharpen and become infinitely compelling. 'Progress is important, and correctly channelled with far-sighted planning, it is possible to preserve the ecology. However, there are men greedy enough to want to push their designs, merely for the satisfaction of financial gain.' His mouth tightened into a thin uncompromising line. 'Ten, twenty years from now, we end up with the type of environment we should most avoid.'

It sounded a formidable collection of interests, and she could only applaud his acumen. 'How old are you?' The words were out before she could stop them.

'Thirty-seven.' One eyebrow slanted with sardonic humour. 'Shall I complete the résumé? My parents emigrated to Australia from Greece when I was very young and settled in Sydney. My father was a restaurateur of some repute, and within a few years he owned one of the finest restaurants in the city. My brother, my sister and I received a formal education which included university, and during the holidays we worked for our parents. Anna helped in the kitchen, and George and I waited on tables. Today only my mother survives. George trained beneath the watchful and talented eye of my father to become head of the restaurant; Anna is married and the proud mother of four children.'

'Do they all live in Sydney?'

'Yes.'

She swallowed nervously. 'I see.'

'What do you see, Samantha?'

His mocking cynicism brought a faint tinge of colour to her cheeks. 'Do they know about me?'

'No.'

'I find that difficult to believe.'

'What has there been to tell them?' Alex parried smoothly, and she rushed into speech.

'And now?'

'You will be presented as my fiancée.'

She looked at him curiously. 'Won't they find that rather strange?'

'That I have a fiancée?'

'Don't be——'

'Facetious?' He drained the last of his coffee, then settled back to regard her with equanimity. 'We are a very close-knit family, yet respect each other's right to lead our own lives. Rest assured they will be delighted I have selected a wife.'

'Usually there's at least a few months between an engagement and the wedding. What will they think?'

'That I'm impatient to observe convention,' Alex drawled, and it took considerable courage to hold his gaze.

'When do you intend enlightening them?'

'Tonight. We're dining with my mother.'

'You're joking—I hope,' Samantha declared fervently. The thought of being presented to the Nicolaos family en masse was nothing less than daunting.

'Don't look so scared,' he murmured. 'I'll be there.'

Her gaze was remarkably even. 'Acting out a part, I suppose.'

One eyebrow slanted with sardonic humour. 'An adoring lover?'

Tawny-gold depths sparked with latent fire. 'You'll never be that!'

A faint shiver shook her slight frame as his eyes narrowed and became hodded, then he stood to his feet.

'Shall we go?'

It was almost five when Alex drew the car to a halt outside the main entrance of his magnificent home, and Samantha entered the spacious foyer to be greeted by a beaming Serafina.

'You enjoyed your drive? Let me take your coat.'

Samantha undid the belt and let the warm garment slip from her shoulders, aware that Alex had shrugged off his sheepskin-lined jacket and had come to stand beside her.

'I'd like to leave in an hour,' he said. 'Can you be ready by then?'

Good heavens, how long did he think it took her to shower, change clothes and attend to her make-up? She could do it in half that time, if need be. Aloud, she murmured a single affirmative, and made for the stairs.

What should she wear? She mentally took stock of her wardrobe and decided the only garment that reached the desired level of sophistication was a calf-length dress in a fine cream wool. Its neckline was a deep-scooped vee with a gathered frill at its edge. With a gold belt at her waist, a slim gold chain at her neck and wrist, and the deft application of make-up, she should achieve a measure of elegance.

After a quick shower, she towelled herself dry, then she moved into the bedroom and slipped into fresh underwear, added pantyhose, and crossed to the mirror to begin applying make-up.

Fifteen minutes later she was ready, and she surveyed the result in the floor-length mirror with critical appraisal. Eyeshadow and mascara highlighted her eyes, making them appear large and luminous, their depths retaining a faintly mysterious quality. Her delicately smooth skin was enhanced by a natural shade of foundation, and skilful use of blusher gave her features a finely balanced look, adding up to a very attractive whole.

Her hair was usually worn in one of two different styles, its length caught up into a knot at the back of her head, or left loose. Tonight she had elected to twist it into an elaborate pleat at her nape in the hope that it would lend added sophistication.

Alex was waiting downstairs, and Samantha faltered to a halt a few feet distant, overwhelmed by the sight of him. Attired in a dark three-piece suit, he made an arresting figure, projecting virile masculinity without any effort at all.

'Am I late?' Her voice sounded faintly breathless, but it wasn't from hurrying, and she mentally chastised herself. It would never do to let him know he had the power to affect her.

'No.' His gaze was appreciative as he moved forward, and she felt her pulse quicken. 'Two things before we leave.' He reached out a hand and dispensed with the carefully contrived pleat at her nape, letting his fingers thread through the length of her hair. 'I like it better loose.'

'It stays tidier in a knot,' she said indignantly, hating his proprietorial manner, and his eyes assumed musing cynicism.

'Did you imagine such a restrained style would add years to your appearance?'

Oh, he was too astute for words! Out loud she returned waspishly, 'Now I'll have to brush it out!'

'Nonsense,' Alex demurred silkily. 'It will do as

it is.' Reaching into the side pocket of his jacket, he withdrew a glittering ring. 'Give me your hand.'

'Why?' she demanded starkly.

'So I can put this on.'

She looked at him in stunned silence as he slid a gold band containing a row of magnificent diamonds on to the appropriate finger. It felt heavy and alien, and she didn't want to wear any symbol attesting his ownership. 'It's a perfect fit. Do I have Sophie to thank for that as well? Or was it a lucky guess?' Anger rose to the surface and her eyes filled with bitterness. 'To have this ready and waiting, you must have been very sure.'

There wasn't a flicker of emotion visible in those dark sardonic features. 'As you surmise,' he drawled with slight mockery, then one eyebrow slanted in silent query. 'Would you like a drink before we leave?'

Undoubtedly it would help bolster her morale and give her sufficient courage for the evening ahead. Yet she rarely touched alcohol, and more than one glass tended to make her feel lightheaded. Inevitably there would be wine with dinner, and she would need all her faculties alert to deal with the Nicolaos family—not to mention the most formidable member of them all, Alex Nicolaos himself!

'No—thank you,' she added politely, inwardly grimacing against a lifetime of instilled good manners.

'Then we'll get on our way.' He took the coat she had folded over her arm and held it out so that she could slip her arms into its sleeves, then he shrugged his shoulders into his own.

'Where does your mother live?'

The Mercedes had left Point Piper and was edging its way east.

'Vaucluse. High on a hill overlooking the harbour.' His tone was brusque, almost pre-occupied, and Samantha fell into an uneasy silence.

If only the evening was over and done with! Being the cynosure of all eyes, having her every word and gesture examined and analysed, was a daunting prospect. Drawing in a deep breath, she expelled it slowly. Perhaps if she smiled a lot, agreed with everyone, she might get by.

A number of butterflies in her stomach began a series of somersaults as the car slowed and eased itself into a wide circular driveway, slowing to a halt behind a low-slung Ferrari.

'It seems we're the last to arrive,' Alex remarked, and he slipped out from behind the wheel to move round and open the door.

Samantha stepped out and walked at his side, mentally preparing herself for what was to come.

'Relax,' he advised quietly. 'You look as if you're about to beard the lions' den.'

'Perhaps I am,' she said shakily, and he shot her a wry smile.

'I assure you they're quite human.'

'The lions?'

His faint mocking laughter echoed in her ears as the front door opened and they were welcomed inside.

'Everyone is assembled in the lounge, if you would care to go through.'

'Thank you, Nathaniel,' Alex smiled at the butler.

Well, here goes, Samantha decided, as ready as she would ever be to meet the fray. A faint bubble of hysterical laughter died in her throat. Anyone would think she was going in to battle!

'Alex! Come in. You are late.'

Samantha was drawn forward without being aware of the moment Alex had caught hold of her hand. Now she felt its firm clasp and unconsciously clutched it, much as if she was drowning and had been proffered a lifeline.

'Nonsense, Mama,' he soothed gently. 'We are precisely on time.'

'Yet everyone else is here,' the elderly matriarch declared imperiously, and Samantha endeavoured to hide her startled surprise.

Mrs Nicolaos was tiny in stature, and dressed entirely in black. Steel-rimmed glasses sat on her small nose, and did nothing to detract from the alert brown eyes gazing fixedly at Samantha, making her feel as if she'd been summed up and categorised in thirty seconds flat!

'Are you not going to introduce this young woman?'

'Of course,' Alex smiled with lazy humour. 'If you will allow me the opportunity.'

'We are waiting.'

'You are frightening the life out of her,' he admonished as he drew Samantha forward, and his mother cast him a dark penetrating look.

'So—you are Samantha,' she began, swinging her attention to the girl at his side. 'Samantha *who*?'

'Evans,' Samantha answered, meeting and holding the older woman's direct gaze.

'You are very young.'

Oh lord, this was worse than she'd envisaged! 'I'm almost twenty.'

'And you are going to marry Alexandros.'

'So he says,' she responded evenly, and saw the faint gleam of amusement in those bright birdlike eyes.

'Ah, told you, did he?'

'I didn't have a say in the matter.'

'Hmm, you have spirit. I like that.'

'My mother,' Alex introduced with wry formality. 'A woman who fondly imagines the combination of age and approaching senility allows her licence to say and do whatever she pleases.'

'Bah! That is so much nonsense!'

'I think it's time Samantha met the rest of us, don't you?' a deep voice drawled, and a slightly younger version of Alex moved forward, his smile alive with dazzling warmth. 'Georgiou, but I answer to George.'

'And I'm Anna,' a light feminine voice announced, then indicated the tall man at her side. 'My husband Nick. We left the children home,' she added with a friendly grin. 'You can meet the horrors at a later time.'

'Horrors? *Horrors?* What manner is that with which to describe my grandchildren?' Mrs Nicolaos reprimanded.

'Because that is exactly what they are,' George declared, suggesting smoothly, 'What would you like to drink, Samantha? I imagine you need one.'

'She's partial to white wine,' Alex intervened, turning slightly towards her. 'A Riesling, darling?'

Darling? 'I'd prefer vermouth, with lemonade.'

A husky chuckle greeted her words, and George glanced towards his brother. 'She has a mind of her own, I see.'

'So it would seem,' Alex agreed, slanting her a musing look.

'Your stepfather was of Greek extraction,' Mrs Nicolaos began. 'Do you speak the language?'

Samantha shook her head, taking time to thank George as she accepted the glass he handed her. 'I believe it is difficult to learn.'

'Do you want to?'

Oh hell, how did she answer that? If she said no, it could offend, and yet——

'I'm sure that if she does, Alex will teach her,' George teased lightly, and she shot him a grateful glance.

'Harumph! And when is this wedding to be?'

'Mama!' Anna protested. 'That is for Alex and Samantha to decide.'

'Soon,' Alex interposed. 'Before the end of the week. Friday, if it can be arranged.'

That soon?

'I don't blame him,' drawled George. 'If she was mine, I'd want to make it legal before she could be tempted by anyone else!'

'Dinner is ready to be served.'

Samantha looked at the man who had quietly entered the room and silently blessed him for the timely interruption. Although afterwards she wasn't sure it made any marked difference, for the conversation continued in a similar vein throughout each of the five courses.

She ate little, and blamed her lack of appetite on Alex's intimidating presence. Although that wasn't strictly fair. His attention was solicitous, and there were occasions when she almost reeled beneath the warm intimacy he accorded her. It became increasingly difficult to maintain his gaze and remain quiescent beneath the light touch of his hand when he let his fingers trail down the length of her arm. His closeness was disturbing, and it irked her unbearably that he was aware of its effect.

At last the meal drew to a close, and it was with considerable relief that Samantha rose from the table and joined the others in the lounge for coffee.

Seconds after being seated she had to hide her surprise when Alex perched his powerful frame on the arm of her chair. The faint spicy tang of his cologne was evident, and she could do nothing about the arm he placed around her shoulders. Her whole body seemed to come alive as each separate nerve-end stirred and began to throb with vibrant fire.

If she leaned slightly sideways her cheek would touch the expensive texture of his suit jacket. As it was, she could feel his body heat, smell the clean mixture of soap and freshly laundered shirt-linen. Every single one of her senses seemed to be acutely attuned to this man, and she was unable to reason why. It was almost as if her subconscious was intent on forcing recognition, and she had to forcibly reject it, rationalising that if she dared to succumb it would be tantamount to madness.

'You won't object if we leave?'

Samantha dimly heard the words and felt an immeasurable sense of relief that the evening was coming to an end. She was tired, a heavy weariness settling on her slim shoulders until it became an intolerable weight. More than anything she wanted to be alone. It had been quite a day, one way and another, and she desperately needed to unravel it all.

'You look tired.'

She glanced up and glimpsed the faint speculative gleam in Mrs Nicolaos' gaze. 'I must admit that I am,' she said quietly. 'Alex and I have been out for most of the day.'

'Then you must go,' the old lady stressed firmly. 'I will see you again soon, at least once before the wedding, I hope?'

'Assuredly, Mama,' Alex told her, his dark eyes

strangely gentle. 'Take care, hmn? Not too much exertion, and plenty of rest.'

'It is a poor state I have reached when I am inclined to take my children's advice!'

'Admit that you love every minute of it,' George teased, moving forward to brush his lips against her temple and smooth back a tendril of white hair. 'We will all leave you to the capable ministrations of the faithful Helena.'

'The party after the wedding——'

'Will be at the restaurant,' George smiled gently. 'As it was for Anna and Nick. Never fear, Alex and I will arrange everything—the guests, the food. All that will be left for you to do is to be there.'

Mrs Nicolaos' expression became strangely vulnerable for an infinitesimal second, then the strength returned, and she swept a compelling glance that was meant to encompass them all. 'You have said you are going—so *go*!'

She was a pussycat, Samantha decided, feeling an odd rush of affection. Wearing the protective shield of a lioness—but a pussycat, nevertheless! The knowledge gave her the courage to bestow a fleeting kiss as she made her farewell, and she was sure the brightness in those dark eyes reflected damp emotion.

'Better than you expected?'

Samantha glanced across at the man seated behind the wheel and was unable to gauge his expression in the car's dim interior.

'You have a nice family.' It was true, no matter how she wanted it otherwise. The eldest son she might hate, but in fairness she was unable to extend that feeling to his mother, George or Anna.

'Of which you will soon become a part.'

'Yes,' she said slowly, and was aware of his swift glance.

'Still so reluctant?'

'What do you expect?'

'Tomorrow I will make the necessary arrangements,' Alex insisted, almost as if she hadn't spoken. 'Sophie will be available to help with whatever shopping is necessary, and Spiros will accompany you both.'

'A jailor and her assistant,' she opined carelessly, and was aware of his anger.

'Careful, Samantha,' he warned silkily. 'I am endeavouring to make the transition as painless for you as possible. If you choose to react with temperament, let me warn that this morning's lesson was nothing to what I can mete out if sufficiently provoked.'

'Tyranny belongs in a bygone era. Today the trend is towards feminism, equality, and the right to be individualistic.'

'So you see me as a tyrant?'

The car had drawn to a halt inside the garage, and she turned towards him. 'What else, when you insist on such a farcical marriage?'

'Ah—you want romance, *love*, to sweep you off your feet, hmn? My dear, I learned long ago that a healthy bank balance is all that is necessary to buy a woman's so-called love,' Alex revealed with ill-concealed mockery, and she retaliated without thought.

'Then you haven't been talking to the right women!'

His husky cynical laugh sounded damning to her ears. 'From memory, we didn't do much talking.'

'One wouldn't imagine so,' Samantha managed with unenviable sarcasm, and reached for the

door-clasp, wanting only to be free of Alex
Nicolaos and all he represented.

Surprisingly he made no attempt to detain her,
and she stood waiting as he unlocked the front
door. When she was halfway up the stairs his voice
bidding her goodnight held the ominous softness
of velvet-encased steel, and unconsciously her
steps quickened, keeping pace with an increased
heartbeat as the mental net he had cast around her
tightened perceptibly.

Despite the warmth of central heating she
shivered, haunted by an image that depicted the
Devil in the guise of her tormentor.

CHAPTER FOUR

THERE was little doubt that Sophie felt awkward and faintly ill at ease when Samantha arrived the following morning. Chauffeured at Alex's insistence by Spiros, they were driven into the city and dropped off outside the huge Centrepoint complex.

'Shall we have coffee first?' Samantha suggested coolly. 'I haven't made a list, and being Alex's accomplice, you probably have more indication of what we're supposed to buy than I do.'

'You're upset,' Sophie declared unnecessarily, and Samantha drew a deep calming breath.

'Wouldn't you be?'

'There's an excellent coffee lounge on one of the upper floors. My sister recommended it. Shall we try and find where it is, then talk?'

Within ten minutes they were seated and two steaming capuccino coffees were placed before them. Sophie extracted cigarettes and a lighter and inhaled with pleasure, almost as if the smoking tube provided some imaginary courage, then she met Samantha's steady gaze with total frankness.

'Alex rang me this morning,' she began without preamble.

'Oh, he did, did he?'

'Samantha——'

'I imagine he discussed our conversation verbatim?'

Sophie regarded the glowing tip of her cigarette, discarded its tip of ash, then took another soothing inhalation. 'He confirmed that you had taken the news badly,' she said evenly, and Samantha broke into expostulatory speech.

'My God! What did you expect? Or *he*, for that matter!' Her eyes were brilliant with angry fire, her face alive with the strength of her emotions. 'In this day and age, how can you expect compliance?' If anything, her eyes became even more brilliant, and her voice held such bitter loathing the older woman flinched visibly from the force of it.

'If you want to retain self-respect——'

'*Self-respect?*' Samantha demanded volubly. 'How can I respect myself? Oh, I agree there's no alternative,' she bit off bitterly. 'Between you, you saw to that. I even helped compound it by choosing a career that's totally useless until I become fully qualified. Without sufficient qualifications or experience, finding employment in any field is virtually impossible.'

'If Alex was an elderly debaucher I might be sympathetic,' Sophie conceded. 'But he's a very eligible man, with a high social standing, and you should be grateful he's offered marriage. He had no moral obligation to do so.'

How did she get through to her? 'I'm being manipulated—coerced, for want of a stronger word,' Samantha corrected vengefully. 'It isn't right!'

'There are any number of women who would positively *leap* to be Alex Nicolaos' wife.'

'Well, I'm not one of them!'

'At the moment you're not thinking clearly,' Sophie insisted.

Samantha closed her eyes, then opened them, and her lips pursed to form a wry grimace. 'What you mean is that I should be realistic. Perhaps I'm not ready for realism!'

'Anyone would imagine Dominic deliberately

contrived to work for a pittance, running up huge debts, simply for the sheer hell of it.' Sophie's gaze held infinite sadness. 'We both know that wasn't true. He loved you, not only because you were your mother's daughter. There wasn't a thing he wouldn't have done for you, or given you, if it was within his power.'

Samantha couldn't say a word; her throat had suddenly become constricted with an emotional lump.

'Don't you see?' the older woman said gently.

'I find it very difficult to accept a loveless marriage,' Samantha began unevenly, shooting Sophie a warning glance. 'And please don't feed me any homilies about the advantages of possessing a wealthy husband!'

'Perhaps the fault lies in part with our upbringing,' Sophie offered. 'We are taught that love is a rare gift from the gods and bestowed on a fortunate few. Therefore it is better for a woman to choose a man who can adequately provide the necessities of life. Time enough after the marriage to achieve an affectionate bond.'

'It sounds so cold, so clinical,' Samantha said shakily.

'You are young—a dreamer of dreams. Reality is food on the table, and money to pay the bills.'

'There has to be more to marriage than that.' Every sane thought screamed an angry rejection of the picture Sophie painted.

'Companionship, fondness, respect—all these qualities are essential ingredients.'

'So you can't see too much wrong with the situation?'

'I can see a lot of things that are right.'

Samantha gave a sigh that behoved great forbearance. There wasn't anything more she

could say or do that would convince Sophie
otherwise. 'In that case, let's add to my
monumental debt and spend some of Alex's
money. Presumably he's given you an indication of
what is to be bought?'

'Something suitable in which to be married is
the major priority, and he has made a few
stipulations.'

'Such as?' Already she could feel resentment
beginning to rankle.

'Evening clothes. You don't have too many, do
you?'

'And I must be seen to be correctly, even
splendidly dressed,' Samantha managed with
considerable sarcasm, and Sophie frowned in
remonstrance.

'Don't underestimate Alex, Samantha,' she
warned. 'He isn't a man it would be wise to trifle
with, or anger unnecessarily.'

True enough. Yet somehow she couldn't accept
all this lightly. Too many factors contrived to
make her aware that women no longer had to be
subservient, nor blindly obedient to a man's every
whim. She had been educated to believe in her own
right as an individual, to contribute something to
the society of mankind, express opinions and
question those which she found difficult to
assimilate.

'Have you finished your coffee?' she asked.

'Yes. Do you want another?'

Samantha shook her head. 'Let's go, shall we?'

By midday they had collected an assortment of
brightly coloured carry-bags, in one of which
reposed a dream of a dress in pale blue wool voile
with draped butterfly sleeves, a bodice embroidered
in the Greek style, its skirt a mass of tiny pleats.
Calf-length, it was the epitome of elegance with a

softly-cut square neckline, and horrendously expensive. But Samantha didn't suffer the mildest of qualms as she presented Alex's credit card in payment. There were shoes, delicate wisps of designer underwear, no less than three evening dresses, and one full-length gown of shimmering aqua silk.

'What now?' Samantha queried as they emerged out on to the pavement and jostled the lunchtime crowds. 'Lunch?'

'Alex suggested we meet him. He has a suite of offices in one of the inner city buildings.'

'Where?' she demanded baldly. She hadn't eaten much for breakfast, and her head was beginning to feel strangely light.

'Not far,' Sophie soothed. 'In the next block, I think. Yes, there it is—that tall building. Seventeenth floor.'

'Good. We can leave these parcels with him. I don't fancy carrying them around all afternoon.'

A slight smile played wryly at the edges of Sophie's mouth. 'I imagine that was his motive for suggesting we call in.'

'Perceptive of him.'

'Yes, wasn't it?'

The entrance foyer was large and covered floor to ceiling in large slabs of grey marble. The directory plaque was impressive with each of its tenants listed in polished brass lettering.

Samantha stepped into the elevator with Sophie and stood in silence as it ascended with electronic precision.

Quite what she expected she was unsure, but to find Nicolaos Consolidated occupied the entire floor was a trifle awe-inspiring. So too was the ultra-sophisticated young woman hovering beside the modern desk module in the outer reception lounge. In fact, she appeared so flawless—dress, make-up and immaculately windswept hairstyle, that for a moment Samantha thought she'd walked in on a commercial modelling layout. If presentation was meant to impress, whoever was responsible for the format should be accorded top marks!

'Miss Evans, Miss Roussos?' The smile was just right, efficient but friendly. 'Mr Nicolaos is expecting you. Please follow me.' A swift glance at their packages brought an expanse of pearly white teeth. 'Shall I take some of those for you?'

Start as you mean to go on, a tiny voice urged, and Samantha summoned an assured smile. 'Would you mind? Alex can bring them home later.'

There wasn't so much as a flicker of emotion on the secretary's face, and Samantha wondered just what she had been told about her employer's visitors.

Alex's office was situated at the far end of a wide corridor, and the secretary discreetly disappeared immediately after announcing their arrival.

Attired in a formal light grey three-piece suit, Samantha had to concede, he looked precisely what he was—very successful.

'You've achieved something, I see.'

Samantha watched as he moved forward and deftly relieved them both of the remainder of their purchases. In surrendering the packages her fingers came into contact with his, and she experienced shock as his touch sent a myriad sensation tingling through her body. His closeness seemed to affect her breathing, and she moved away to stand some feet distant.

'A drink, Sophie? Samantha?' Alex enquired

smoothly. 'Or would you prefer to wait until lunch?'

Lord, if she touched so much as a drop of alcohol now she'd hardly be responsible for her actions! 'Not for me,' she refused firmly, shooting Sophie a querying glance.

'No, nor me, thank you, Alex.'

The packages were locked into a nearby cupboard, and he moved towards his desk, flipped a switch, and spoke into the intercom. 'I'll be out for a few hours, Rebecca. Take any messages, and tell Thwaite I'll be available after three.' He glanced up and cast both women an enquiring glance. 'No feminine tidying up to do before we leave? No? Then let us be on our way.' He moved across the room and opened the door, and his features were politely inscrutable.

What did she expect? Samantha thought crossly. A chaste kiss, a show of pretence in deference to their forthcoming marriage? But then there was no one around to fool.

The elevator had seemed perfectly roomy as it had transported them up barely twenty minutes previously, but now Samantha felt decidedly claustrophobic as it descended swiftly to the ground floor. Alex seemed to fill its confines, his height and breadth a powerful force that made her supremely aware of each separate breath she took.

'I thought we'd walk,' he indicated as they emerged on to the pavement. 'The restaurant I have in mind is in the next block.'

Samantha endeavoured to assure herself it was merely courtesy that was responsible for him taking hold of her elbow. If she objected it would sound churlish, especially as he had afforded Sophie the same gesture.

Food! She hadn't realised just how hungry she

was! The delicate array of tantalising aromas assailed her nostrils, and her stomach gave a protesting anticipatory murmur as a solicitous attendant escorted them to a corner table.

'A white wine, Samantha?'

Dared she? Perhaps not, with several more hours' shopping ahead. 'Fruit juice,' she decided, tempering her refusal with a slight smile. 'Orange, if possible.'

'Keeping a clear head?'

His query was faintly mocking, and she let her lips widen into a seemingly sweet smile. 'I'd hate to spend your money unnecessarily from being too befuddled to make the right selection.'

'Perhaps you need my assistance?'

She gave a light laugh that was totally without humour. 'Oh, I'm sure you'd find the time-consuming task of choosing make-up an enthralling experience,' she allowed dryly, and was unprepared for his husky laughter.

'Touché! Perhaps we should confine ourselves to what is on the menu.'

In the end Samantha was unable to resist a starter of prawns sautéed in a delicate garlic sauce, followed by breast of chicken and a crisp salad. From habit she declined dessert and opted for black coffee.

'The ceremony is arranged for Friday afternoon at five o'clock,' Alex informed her inflexibly, ignoring Samantha's startled gasp of surprise.

'We've bought almost everything,' Sophie declared, adding with a slight sigh, 'The next few days should finish it off.'

'Then all that remains is to get me to the church on time,' said Samantha with unaccustomed flippancy.

'Register office.'

Of course. It would be almost an obscenity to have their vows consecrated in a house of God. Suddenly she wished it was all over. Not so much the ceremony, or even the family party afterwards. It was the moment Alex would possess her body that bothered her. *Bothered* seemed too mild a word. He was an unknown entity—infinitely dangerous, and someone to be treated with care.

Care. With it, she might be accorded a gentle seduction. Without it, he would have no hesitation in conducting a punishing violation.

Suddenly she shivered, her mind trapped by innumerable demons, and her expression for an infinitesimal second became hauntingly vulnerable.

'Cold?'

Samantha forced herself to meet that hard implacable gaze. 'A ghost just walked over my grave.'

'Dominic?'

Oh, he was too perceptive by far! 'Perhaps he was trying to warn me.'

'Really, Samantha,' Sophie chided. 'You're becoming far too morbid!'

Samantha directed a level glance. 'Forgive me,' she said heavily. 'I don't share your philosophy of life.'

Alex leaned well back in his chair and extracted cigarettes and lighter, removed one and lit it with studied care before glancing coolly across the table.

'Come back to the office when you've finished your shopping,' he directed. 'I'll take you home.'

'What about Sophie?'

'We'll see her safely into a taxi,' he said imperturbably as Sophie made a protesting murmur.

'And afterwards?' Samantha found herself

asking without any regret at all, and saw his veiled
glance.

'I have a quiet evening in mind.'

'Really? I'd like to go out,' she said starkly. 'A
movie, the theatre—anywhere.' A thought presented
itself and she flashed him a brilliant smile. 'I love
dancing. Perhaps you could indulge me?' Devilry
had to be responsible for the words that followed.
'Or aren't crowded discos your scene?'

'Not usually.' His dark glance pierced hers, and it
took considerable courage to hold it unwaveringly.
'However, I've no objection to a nightclub.'

'Really, Samantha!' Sophie reproved. 'It isn't
like you to behave irrationally.'

'Good heavens,' she managed lightly, glancing
from one to the other, 'I've led a fairly subdued
sort of social existence up until now. With no more
study to consume my time, I'd like to live a little.
That is,' she added sweetly, turning slightly
towards Alex, 'if you feel you can stand the pace?'

A faint gleam of amusement lit his eyes. 'I'm not
quite in my dotage yet,' he drawled, and she
returned without thought,

'Your friends will think you've gone in for
cradle-snatching.'

'Samantha! That was uncalled for. You must
apologise at once.'

'Must I?' There was no sense to the way she was
behaving, and part of her deplored it. 'Alex is
seventeen years my senior—old enough to have
fathered me.'

'I don't know what has come over you!'

'Don't you, Sophie?' she queried a trifle sadly.
'You're a very attractive woman, yet you've never
chosen to marry. I don't have the opportunity to
choose—not even the man. It's all been taken care
of for me. Yet I'm supposed to sit here like a polite

little schoolgirl and exchange pleasantries—even show some enthusiasm for what lies ahead of me.' Her eyes began to glitter with ill-suppressed emotion. 'Well, let me tell you that inside I feel like picking up that delectable-looking mousse and tipping it over your head.' Her gaze swung towards Alex. 'Yours, too!'

A muscle tensed along his jaw, and for a second she thought she saw humour twitch the edge of his lips, but it was gone in an instant, and afterwards she could only think she'd imagined it.

'Hardly advisable,' he drawled, and she flashed back,

'No, it wouldn't be, would it?'

'You're almost causing a scene,' Sophie protested, scandalised, and Samantha retorted,

'And that would never do!'

'Save all that angry fire for when we're alone,' cautioned Alex with implacable calm, and she became incensed.

'So that you can give me another lesson in punishment?' Derision etched her delicate features. 'Oh, forgive me—we mustn't shock Sophie.'

'I imagine Sophie would approve any method I employ in taming a shrewish wife.'

He *was* amused! 'Oh, let's get out of here,' Samantha muttered wretchedly.

'Not yet. Sophie hasn't finished her dessert, and the waiter is about to serve coffee.'

There was nothing for it but to sit quietly, and she refrained from uttering so much as a further word. If she opened her mouth she'd end up saying a whole lot of things that would be difficult to retract. Wild irrational anger was one thing, but having to deal with its consequences had no appeal whatsoever.

It was a further half-hour before they left, and

almost as soon as Alex left them Sophie burst into reprehensive speech.

'Don't,' Samantha said fiercely, momentarily closing her eyes. 'Put it down to childish retaliation, and leave it—please. I couldn't bear to hear what I know you're going to say.'

Sophie was obviously lost for words. 'You've always been so well-behaved,' she breathed at last, and Samantha threw a wry glance.

'I've never felt the need to *mis*behave.'

'Do you realise just how fortunate you are?'

She drew in a deep steadying breath. 'Oh yes,' she managed dryly. 'Alex saw fit to demonstrate just that point.' In a minute she would scream, she knew it. 'Look, let's go in search of the cosmetic counter at David Jones, shall we? That is, if we can find David Jones,' she finished wryly.

'It's in the next block,' Sophie informed her dispassionately, and Samantha lengthened her stride with natural agility, forcing the older woman to move more quickly.

'The lights—we'll just catch them.'

'Really, what's the hurry?' Sophie demanded, slightly breathless.

'I need another dress.' The idea had occurred almost as she spoke. 'A nightclub deserves something sensational.'

'But you already have three,' Sophie protested. 'Samantha, I must caution you against angering Alex——'

'I'm only pandering to his ego.' She offered a brilliant smile that did nothing to reassure. 'An older man adores squiring a pretty young thing around town. The entire object is to attract attention.' The outfit she had in mind would certainly do that, and more!

'You're planning something, I can tell.'

'Then you're very astute,' Samantha responded airily. 'The thought really hadn't crossed my mind.'

It took two hours of searching to find what she wanted, and nothing Sophie said proved a discouragement. Fate had taken an unkind hand in forcing this diabolical marriage, but nothing decreed that she had to meekly accept it. Alex Nicolaos might hold all the aces, but she intended giving him a run for his money.

Consequently it was after five when both women entered the elevator and pushed the button for the seventeenth floor. Each carried a brightly-hued carry-bag, as well as a collection of parcels.

'You've spent a lot of money.'

Samantha glanced at Sophie and gave a careless shrug. 'Alex didn't impose any limitations.'

'Don't attempt revenge,' Sophie cautioned with a worried frown.

Samantha kept a cursory eye on the instrument panel, and moved forward as the elevator slowed to a halt. 'Whatever gave you that idea?'

The receptionist showed them through to Alex's secretary's office, and Rebecca's greeting was without fault as she rose to her feet. 'Mr Nicolaos has a client with him, but if you'll follow me, I'll take you through to his private lounge and he'll join you as soon as he's free.'

Situated at the end of the corridor, and adjacent to Alex's office, the lounge commanded a superb view over sprawling city buildings to the harbour. Tinted glass precluded the need for curtains, and the décor bore the stamp of perfect co-ordination from the heavy woven tweed-effect carpet to the deep-brown soft leather chairs. It was a masculine room; strong and dominant, like its owner.

'Can I get you a drink?' Rebecca crossed to a

well-stocked bar and paused expectantly, ready to attend to their needs.

'A Martini would be lovely, thank you,' Sophie acquiesced gratefully, and Samantha requested brandy, lime and lemonade.

It was fifteen minutes before the adjoining door opened and Alex entered the room. His presence had an electrifying effect that made Samantha reach for her glass and drain its remaining contents.

'Another?' He looked vital, totally in command, and his movements as he crossed towards her were lithe and easy.

'Please,' she murmured, holding out her glass. 'Sophie?'

'One was sufficient.'

If Alex discerned the faint tinge of censure he gave no sigh as he refilled Samantha's glass and poured one for himself.

'We'll take you home, Sophie,' he said some twenty minutes later as they took the elevator to the basement car park. 'Taxis are rare and few between at this hour.'

'I can take the ferry to Manly,' the older woman protested. 'It would be no trouble.'

'Not at all.'

Alex stowed the packages in the boot of the Mercedes, while Samantha slid into the narrow rear seat. It didn't make sense to sit beside Alex and have Sophie clamber in and out unnecessarily.

Peak hour traffic had subsided, but the inner city roads were still choked with cars and it took half an hour to deposit Sophie outside her sister's suburban home, and almost the same amount of time to return to Point Piper.

'Spiros will take care of all the packages,' Alex drawled as he slid from behind the wheel, and Samantha sent him a cool glance.

'If you're implying that I've overdone the shopping spree, why not say so?'

'My dear Samantha,' he drawled with silky detachment, 'you're an attractive young woman. Why should I complain if you've chosen to heighten your natural beauty?'

Put like that, it seemed as if she'd deliberately set out to please him, when the opposite was true. Damn! The victory she had thought to be hers had been very neatly reversed.

'I've booked a table for seven-thirty.' Alex slid back the cuff of his jacket. 'Is half an hour sufficient for you to shower and change? Or shall I ring and say we'll be delayed?'

Samantha gave an imperceptible shrug. 'I'll be ready.'

And she was, with a minute to spare. Perhaps it was just as well she had not had time to reflect, otherwise her courage might have flown. The swift glance she had cast her mirrored image had brought forth a wry grimace as she viewed the slinky gown. Deep ruby red and slit to the thigh, it was something few women could wear with dignity. In fact, dignity was the last word one could use as a descriptive! On stage it would be a knock-out; in a nightclub such as Alex would choose, it could only draw every eye in the room. Now it was carefully hidden by a coat; the unveiling would come later, when it was too late for Alex to do anything about it.

The décor was elegant and restrained, Samantha noted as they entered the nightclub foyer, and it needed only a glance to realise that the patrons were among the élite of the city's social echelon. The table they were shown was well situated, neither too near nor too far from the dance-floor.

'May I take your coat?'

Samantha felt a moment of near panic, then after a brief hesitation she surrendered it to the attentive waiter before taking the seat he held out for her. She was almost afraid to glance across the table, but *savoir faire* was essential in this particular charade, and her eyes were startlingly clear as she met Alex's dark inscrutable gaze.

'Definitely chosen with a view to elevating a man's blood pressure,' he drawled.

It took considerable effort to smile, but she managed it. 'I thought you'd like it.'

'There isn't a man here who doesn't envy me,' he said dryly as he consulted the wine-list and made a selection. 'Are you willing to leave the choice to me, or do you have any particular preference?'

He'd succeeded in making her actions appear childish, which if she were honest, they were. If she had any sense she would tread very lightly, perhaps even resign herself to making the best of a bizarre situation. It wouldn't take much effort to enjoy the trappings that marriage to a wealthy man would afford.

'Oh, you choose,' she dismissed quietly.

One eyebrow arched wryly. 'Rather daring of you.'

'Not really. Your taste has to be impeccable.'

'My dear Samantha! A compliment?'

Her gaze was steady. 'Stop playing with me, Alex.'

'Likewise,' he drawled with sardonic cynicism.

Whatever made her think she could best him? She had to be mad to even try! With a hand that shook slightly she picked up her glass and savoured its contents, then replaced it down on to the table. What did one discuss? she contemplated a trifle wildly as the silence between them yawned into a despairing void. Only the naïve resorted to such topics as the weather, or the state of the nation, yet what else was there? She could hardly blurt out the uppermost question in her mind, one that was beginning to assume alarming proportion as each hour drew ever nearer towards their marriage. Looking at him now, it was hard to imagine he possessed one gentle bone in his body. Possession—that was precisely what she was. *His*, to do whatever he chose. Suddenly she shivered.

'Cold?'

She let her eyes sweep up to meet his, and almost flinched at the cool mockery evident. He couldn't read her mind, surely? Was she that transparent? 'No,' she said evenly. 'But I'd like to dance.'

'Why not?' He rose to his feet and moved round to hold her chair, leading her towards the small dance-floor with courteous detachment.

His arms held her firmly, and for such a powerfully-built man he moved with remarkable grace, his steps matching hers with a fluidity that made dancing a pleasure.

As to the rest of it, she felt disinclined to explore the way her body responded to his. Some devious alchemy had to be responsible for the traitorous pulse thudding at the base of her throat. It didn't stop there. Her breathing seemed to be affected as well, and every inch of skin tingled alive, heightening her senses and making her feel achingly aware of him.

The food was excellent, although afterwards she had little recollection of what they ate, and it was almost midnight when Alex declared his intention to leave.

'So soon?' Samantha queried with a winsome smile. 'Afraid I might become Cinderella?'

His eyes held wry cynicism as he held out her

coat. 'I have an early appointment, followed by two corporate meetings in the morning.'

'Ah, yes, the wheels of big business. One can only imagine you need adequate sleep to cope with it.'

'Careful,' he cautioned softly, and she turned towards him.

'Do you usually escort your—er—lady friends home this early?'

'That depends.'

'Really?'

'On whether I spend what remains of the night in their bed,' he finished silkily, and his eyes fixed deliberately on the faint blush that coloured her cheeks.

Samantha didn't offer a word by way of comment as she accompanied him out to the car, and comfortably seated, she stared out at the encroaching darkness as Alex sent the vehicle moving smoothly forward.

As soon as it drew to a halt inside the garage she reached for the doorclasp and slid out to stand waiting as Alex locked up.

The sleeve of his jacket brushed her arm as he inserted the key, and she forced herself to step inside the house when all her instincts screamed for her to run.

At the base of the stairs she paused momentarily. 'Thank you for taking me out.' The words sounded stilted, and she cast him a swift glance, noting the faint mockery evident.

'So—thank me.'

'I just did.' Why did she feel so apprehensive? Rather like a mouse suddenly confronted by a lion. And why stand here, almost as if she was waiting for him to kiss her? 'Goodnight.'

'Oh no, my reluctant fiancée,' he drawled. 'That

won't do at all.' He reached out and caught hold of her slim shoulders.

'It's late,' she stammered, helpless in the force of his attraction, and he smiled.

'Only a short while ago you implied that the night was young.'

'I'd like to go to bed,' Samantha said in desperation.

'So would I,' Alex declared dryly, and she flashed quickly,

'Not mine. Not yet.'

One eyebrow rose in open mockery. 'You wear a dress that issues an obvious sexual invitation. Chosen,' he paused deliberately, 'to tantalise. Most men would insist that you deliver,' he ended with dangerous softness.

She swallowed nervously. 'A few days from now you'll have the right to make me.' She met his gaze with unblinking steadiness. 'Surely you can wait until then?'

'Are you going to insist that I do?'

A pulse started hammering in her throat, and it took all her courage to remain quiescent. 'I doubt I could stop you.' Fire sparked from her eyes, giving them a tawny glow. 'But I'd hate you for ever if you did!'

Dark eyes above her own gleamed with sardonic humour. 'And will you hate me any less, two nights from now?'

'Probably not.' Her chin lifted fractionally. 'I'm damned if I'll fall into your arms like some docile lamb!'

'More like a cornered vixen, hmn?'

Oh, he was amused! Without thought her hand sped towards his face, only to be caught in a bone-crushing grip.

For a few timeless seconds it seemed as if he

would strike her, then he caught hold of her other hand and forced them both behind her back, propelling her forward until the length of her body melded with his.

There was nothing she could do to prevent the slow descent of his head, and his mouth closed over hers with relentless pressure. Clenched teeth didn't remain an impenetrable barrier for long, and she gave a silent moan of entreaty as he began a deep ravishing invasion.

If it was meant as a punishment, it succeeded, and when he released her she almost swayed with pent-up reaction.

'Remember one thing,' Alex ground harshly. 'Hit, and I'll hit back. Whatever coin you choose, I'll repay it two-fold!'

His face became an indistinct blur as tears clouded her vision, and without a word she turned and ran quickly up the stairs to her room. There was no lock to bar his entry, and she leant against the door as deep jagged breaths tore through her body.

It was a long time before she moved away and made ready for bed, and only in the early dawn hours did she lose hold on wakefulness and slip into a deep troubled sleep.

CHAPTER FIVE

THE register office was without character, the celebrant's voice intoning the chosen words with a total lack of emotion.

Samantha wondered wildly how many times he repeated those same phrases in a day. He probably knew them off by heart, and was possibly bored at having such a tedious job.

The ring Alex slipped on to her nerveless finger was wide and gold, and felt like a miniature manacle.

There was only Alex's immediate family present, and Sophie. Gathered together in a room designed to seat up to fifty people, seven looked remarkably inadequate.

Despite the informality apparent, Alex, together with Sophie, had been adamant Samantha dress for the occasion, and deciding she might as well be hanged for a sheep as for a lamb, she had chosen a traditional gown in cream silk and lace, its design deceptively simple.

Alex looked arresting—there was no other superlative suitable to describe him. From his handstitched shoes to his impeccably tailored frame, he exuded all the characteristics of a successful businessman, portraying dynamic masculinity without any effort at all.

At the Double Bay restaurant there were photographs taken by the dozen, utilising both formal and informal settings, until Samantha felt dazed by the flashing bulbs.

There were a large number of guests present, to

whom she was individually introduced, so that by the end of it the polite smile she had summoned seemed fixed and stilted.

The meal was a gourmet's delight, each course an exquisite complement to the one preceding and succeeding it, and the finest champagne flowed without restraint.

There was little doubt it was a joyful celebration, a tribute to the marriage of the eldest son and head of the Nicolaos family.

They were the centre of attention, and Alex gave every appearance of being a devoted husband. He hardly moved from her side, and if she hadn't known different, she might have been swayed by his smile, the frequent touch of his hand at her waist. Only she was aware of the dark purpose behind this diabolical marriage, and Sophie. Except that Sophie could be guaranteed to maintain silence, for Samantha's benefit as well as her own.

An hour became two, followed all too quickly by another two, until it was time for them to leave. Samantha grew increasingly nervous, despite an attempt to mask it, and it rankled unbearably that Alex was aware of her agitation. The faint cynicism evident in those dark eyes mocked her desire to escape, silently ensuring that there would be none. Tonight his possession would be complete, with or without her consent.

Beneath a cloud of confetti and rice they escaped to the Mercedes parked out front, and within minutes Alex had fired the engine, sending the vehicle forward with restrained speed until it reached the main road leading towards Point Piper.

The tension began to build up inside her, manifesting itself as a tangible pain that started in her stomach and spread until her entire body seemed to throb with it. A hollow laugh rose and died in her throat. Faced with an alternative, she wasn't sure leaping from the moving car would have worse consequences than those which lay ahead of her! Then reason surfaced with the knowledge that such foolishness would only serve to delay the inevitable. Far better to get it over and done with. She wasn't the first woman to be placed in such an invidious position, and she probably wouldn't be the last.

Oh God, why *me*? she groaned inwardly, cursing afresh the circumstances that had contrived to change her chosen destiny.

The car slowed and turned into the driveway, its wheels crunching softly on the gravel as it paused momentarily for the garage doors to automatically open, then it slid inside and came to a halt.

The overhead light provided more than adequate illumination and Samantha slipped out from her seat and waited while Alex moved towards the side door.

A few multi-coloured pieces of confetti showered to her feet, and she brushed a hand over her hair in an effort to dislodge any remaining.

'Stand still,' Alex commanded, leaning forward to remove those she hadn't been able to reach.

His close proximity robbed the breath from her throat, and she stood in paralysed silence as he lifted a hand and raked it through his hair, then removed his jacket in an effort to be rid of any minuscule grains of rice.

Hooking the jacket over one shoulder, he inserted his key and held open the door, his dark gaze deliberately inscrutable as she preceded him inside.

The necessity to say something assumed importance, and she uttered the first thing that came into her head.

'No need to guess what happens next.' As an attempt at humour it failed miserably.

'Despite being regarded as the Devil incarnate,' he drawled silkily, 'I don't go in for rape.'

'Oh?' she said jerkily. 'How else do you imagine you'll achieve your objective?'

Alex studied her silently for several heartstopping seconds, then offered musingly, 'It's called subtle persuasion.'

'Guaranteed never to fail, I suppose,' Samantha threw a trifle wildly, and saw his eyes narrow fractionally.

'You'd be wise to accept it. Fighting will only worsen the situation.'

Her eyes swung up to meet his. 'Where do you want me? I believe the phrase is—"my bed, or yours"?'

'We'll occupy the master bedroom suite at the far end of the hall,' drawled Alex. 'Serafina moved all your clothes this afternoon.'

She digested that in silence, then offered, 'Do I walk to my doom, or do you intend carrying me in true bridal fashion?'

'Which would you prefer?' he arched sardonically, and she snapped back,

'My preference would be to walk out of the door, but that's impossible, isn't it?'

Alex leant out and captured her chin. 'You know it.'

Tawny-gold depths sparkled with molten fire. 'Then let's get it over and done with.'

'Such enthusiasm,' Alex mocked. 'Afraid you might enjoy it?'

'Never!'

'Are you issuing a challenge?'

cleanliness stretched over his ribcage, then tapered down to lean hips and a taut stomach.

Samantha's gaze stopped there, then slid slowly upwards as his arms imprisoned her. To continue fighting him was madness, yet anything else had to be capitulation.

Slowly she let her head rest against his chest, turning her face slightly so that her lips brushed against the thick mat of chest hair, then she took careful aim and bit him, *hard.*

His harsh oath gave momentary satisfaction, then he flung her on to the bed without any pretence of gentleness, trapping her body with his own as she rolled and tried to scramble to her feet.

'Oh no, little wildcat,' Alex growled emotively, catching both her hands and holding them with one of his above her head. 'A fair fight is one thing, but physical violence is quite another!'

'What the hell do you call what you just did to me?' Samantha cried out in anguish.

'You bit first.'

'I'll probably be scarred for life,' she said hatefully, and saw his mouth twist wryly.

'I was very careful not to use my teeth—unlike you.'

Her eyes were drawn as if by a magnet to where she had bitten him, and a deep shudder raked her body as she saw the circle of bleeding cuts made by her teeth.

Stupid futile tears filled her eyes. 'I hate what you're doing to me.'

'Then hate me,' he said dispassionately. 'Emotion will have nothing to do with the conception of our child.'

His face became a blur. 'Stop torturing me!'

'Take what is so reluctantly offered, yet seek to give nothing in return?'

'Go to hell!' Samantha whispered shakily.

'Maybe taking you there, once,' he uttered harshly, 'will teach you that pleasure is infinitely preferable to pain.'

'You've hurt me enough!'

His glance lanced through her. 'Then stop playing childish games.'

'What am I supposed to do?' she hissed furiously. 'Simply lie here and imagine some dream lover is invading my body?'

'Reality will soon dispense with the dream,' Alex told her drily, then his mouth settled over hers, brutal and infinitely possessive.

She began to struggle in earnest, fear lending unknown strength as she fought to be free of him. Somehow she managed to free one hand, and she lashed out at him, pummelling his back, shoulders, anywhere she could reach. When that made no impression, she raked her nails down his ribcage and achieved some satisfaction from his swift intake of breath.

'Little hellcat,' he growled, lifting his mouth fractionally to subject her to a dark emotive appraisal.

His body crushed hers, his long legs successfully trapping her own so that any movement she tried to make could only be minimal.

'I hate you, *hate* you, do you understand?'

His eyes filled with icy anger, and his expression became so harshly forbidding she almost cried out.

'Then you shall have reason to hate me.' His pitiless resolve was unmistakable, and even as she began to plead with him, he caught hold of her hand, moving to lie on his side, facing her.

Slowly, with deliberate featherlightness, he began to trace an evocative path over the soft contours of her body, arousing each separate

sensory nerve-end until she began to moan an
entreaty for him to desist. Nothing she said would
make him stop as he began to explore each hidden
crevice, then not content, he lowered his mouth to
her breast to tease and tantalise one burgeoning
peak before crossing to render a similar assault to
the other.

When Samantha thought she could stand no
more, his head moved lower, trailing down until
she gasped at the brazen degree of intimacy he
seemed intent on taking, then she did cry out in
shocked disbelief, her voice a husky guttural plea
as she begged and alternately pleaded with him.

Her whole body seemed to pulse with liquid fire
as sensation after sensation washed over her, and
she became mindless, lost in a world of sensuality
that knew no bounds. She was floating, caught
high on an emotional tide so intense there was no
room for anything but the swirling satiating vortex
into which she had been drawn.

His mouth covered hers, stifling the cry that
rose in her throat as he effected a penetrating
thrust, then he began to move, creating a deep
throbbing ache that swelled until she became
caught up in the rhythmic pattern of his
possession.

It was a long time before she was aware of her
surroundings, and the slow descent to normalcy
brought a whole gamut of emotions none of which
were enviable. Worst of all, she was consumed
with resentment at having been made frighteningly
aware of her own sensuality.

Alex had made sure of it, she thought bitterly,
deliberately pacing his sexual pleasure with the
awakening tumult of her own, and such a
ravaging, soul-destroying assault was something
she could never forgive

'I hate you.' The words were little more than a fierce vehement whisper, and brought forth a husky chuckle from the mouth mere inches above her own.

'Poor Samantha,' he mocked lightly as his lips sought a particularly vulnerable hollow at the base of her throat.

Hands that had clung only minutes before now sought to push him away. 'Have you finished?' she queried icily.

'For the moment.'

Oh God! How often did he intend to subject her to this sort of physical invasion? If it was to be every night, she doubted she could bear it!

Suddenly weary, she turned her head on the pillow, seeking its comforting softness as Alex moved to lie beside her. Her whole body seemed to be one large pulsating ache, and she felt bruised, inside and out. More than anything she wanted to sleep, to attempt to blot out, albeit temporarily, the sweet savagery of his lovemaking.

Moving cautiously, she slid from the bed and made her way to the bathroom. The large capacious tub looked infinitely inviting, and ignoring the shower cubicle, she inserted the plug, opened the taps and reached for the bath essence, choosing the container nearest without even consulting its label.

Minutes later she stepped into the scented water and sank down until it lapped soothingly round her shoulders, then she picked up a sponge and began systematically to remove every trace of Alex's possession. By the time she had finished every square inch of skin tingled from her dedicated ministrations. She felt deliciously warm and drowsy, and the temptation to close her eyes was immense.

'Little fool!'

The harsh words intruded into her subconscious, bringing her awake even as hard hands caught and lifted her from the water.

Samantha felt strangely disorientated, and she stared at him silently, her eyes wide and totally lacking in guile.

'What the hell were you trying to do?' Alex demanded harshly as he dragged a towel from near by and wrapped it round her.

'Not attempting to drown myself,' she managed shakily, and bit her lip as he towelled her with a briskness that was totally uncaring. 'Do you have to be so rough?' she choked. 'I'm not an animal in need of a rub-down!'

'I could slap you, do you know that?' His voice throbbed with emotive anger, and his eyes were dark and intense.

'Please don't.' To her utter horror her lower lip began to tremble, and she blinked rapidly against the prick of tears that threatened to well behind her eyes.

His husky expletive brought a tinge of colour to her cheeks, which only deepened as he threw the towel on to the floor, and she crossed her arms across her breasts in defence against his raking scrutiny.

Slowly Alex reached out and caught hold of her hands, forcing them apart. His eyes narrowed as he took in the faint bruising apparent on her delicate skin, the soft pink smudges on her breasts.

Summoning as much dignity as she could muster, she lifted her chin and met his dark enigmatic gaze. 'Satisfied?' A cold blind anger began to surface, clouding reason. 'Or do you intend manhandling me again?'

For a moment she thought he meant to punish

her, and she saw a muscle tense along his jaw as he sought to control his temper.

'Go to bed.' His voice was hard and curiously expressionless.

All her instincts screamed out that she should comply, but she was damned if she would give in like a meek obedient mouse. Besides, she wanted to complete her toilette. 'I will, when I'm ready.' She drew a deep calming breath and shot him an icy glare. 'Will you please get out of here?' Her tawny eyes raked his cruelly-set features. 'Or am I permitted no privacy at all?'

Alex didn't say a word, his powerfully-muscled frame portraying a potent strength against which she could provide little resistance, and it became increasingly difficult to maintain defiance.

Then he moved, stepping past her as he entered the shower cubicle, and as water burst from the wall-nozzle Samantha turned hastily back towards the marble-topped cabinet, extracted the items she needed, then completed her toilette in record time.

In the bedroom she began a rapid search for a nightgown, opening and closing drawers in quick succession. Where the devil had Serafina put them, for heaven's sake!

'Looking for something?'

Samantha became filled with helpless frustration at the sound of that hateful drawling voice. 'My nightgown,' she flung tersely, and glancing up she encountered his mocking smile in the mirror. She was so angry she almost shook with it. 'Maybe you're used to sleeping totally naked, but I'm not!' She pulled out another drawer, but it was empty, and stupid tears blurred her vision. There were only two drawers remaining, and with her luck it was bound to be the last. It was, and she extracted the sought-after slither of silk and lace with swift jerky movements, then pulled it over her head, supremely conscious that he was observing her every action.

'A little late for modesty, wouldn't you say?'

Somehow she had to turn and walk to that huge bed and slip beneath the covers. To do so seemed synonymous with unwanted quiescence, and she hesitated, almost swaying on her feet as her eyes slid slowly towards Alex.

'Don't look at me like that!'

One eyebrow rose with sardonic cynicism. 'How would you have me look at you?' His lips moved to form a twisted smile. 'You're a very beautiful young woman.'

'I don't feel beautiful,' she flung incautiously, and watched with mesmerised fascination as he moved slowly towards her.

Reaching out a hand, he tilted her chin, his eyes dark and curiously watchful. 'How do you feel, Samantha?'

'Does your ego demand a post-mortem?' Her eyes flashed with brilliant fire as she raked his features. 'Am I supposed to swoon and assure you you were divine?' She was goaded almost to the point of hysteria. 'I hated it, do you understand? I've never felt so degraded, so utterly——' she faltered to a halt, foundering for words, and he prompted silkily,

'*Possessed?* What did you expect? A gentle wooing, after fighting like a little wildcat?'

'You behaved like a—a barbaric *savage!*'

'Indeed?' A hint of steel entered his voice. 'Be grateful I kept a rein on my temper.'

The truth of his words was something she refused to concede, and suddenly she felt inexplicably weary. 'I'd like to go to sleep.' Her eyes seemed incredibly large as she met his narrowed gaze, unconsciously pleading before the lashes fluttered down to cast dark shadows against her pale features.

Without a word Alex shifted slightly, swinging her into his arms to carry her without effort to the bed. There was a curious gentleness apparent as he laid her down, then he pulled up the covers and crossed round to slip in beside her.

Samantha was aware of the moment he switched off the bedside lamp, and it wasn't until she heard the steady rise and fall of his breathing that she gave in to the luxury of tears. In a slow-falling trickle, they spilled to roll down her cheeks and soak her pillow before sheer exhaustion provided a blissful oblivion.

Samantha stirred restlessly, caught in that no-man's land between sleep and wakefulness and not wanting either. She felt as if she was buried in a cocoon of enveloping warmth, lulled by the soft rhythmic thud pulsing close to her ear, and the desire to sink deeper into the security it represented was almost impossible to resist.

Then returning memory brought an awareness of where she was, and her lashes reluctantly flickered, then swept slowly open.

The room glowed with the soft light of an early dawn, muted by drawn curtains covering the large windows, and she lay perfectly still as she became attuned to her surroundings.

A heavy weight anchored her to the bed, and she cautiously examined the cause, letting her eyes travel down to the arm that lay across her waist, then lifting them slowly until she met the dark slumbrous gaze of her indomitable husband.

'So,' Alex mused quietly. 'At last you wake.'

She must have unconsciously sought the warmth

of his body in the night—that, or Alex had drawn her close. One thing was clear. She couldn't remain there.

'What time is it?'

'Seven.' His eyes assumed a mocking gleam as she endeavoured to extricate herself. 'In such a hurry to get up?' He rolled on to his side, resting an elbow on the pillow to prop his head as he faced her, then he lifted a hand and smoothed her hair back from her face.

There was latent sensuality in the gesture, and Samantha shrank back as his fingers trailed the length of her finely-moulded jaw and down her throat to caress the soft hollows there, before slipping lower, edging the delicate lace aside as he brushed one dusky peak, then sought to bring its burgeoning bud into full arousal.

'No!' The husky denial left her lips even as he moved to trap her mouth with his own, invading its sweetness with hardening desire.

'Take this damned thing off,' Alex growled softly as his hands slithered down to her self-encased waist, and when she shook her head his lips twisted to form a wry smile. 'I'd hate to tear it off you.'

Her eyes came alive with bitterness. 'Your money bought it.'

Without a word he caught hold of the delicate lace and rendered the edges apart in one easy movement, right down to its hem.

'Oh! You unspeakable fiend!' Her hands flew to cover her breasts, and he unhurriedly caught hold of each hand, holding them together in a merciless grip as he conducted a raking appraisal.

He took his time, making no effort to dispel the tension clearly visible in her eyes, his gaze becoming narrowed and faintly condemning as he examined each darkening bruise, then slowly he bent his head and brushed his lips across each contusion in turn.

A strange mixture of apprehension and defiance rose within, intermingled with deepening awareness, causing her breasts to rise and fall with increasing agitation. She opened her mouth to cry out that she wanted none of it, but her throat seemed locked in the grip of an agonising constriction.

Lower and lower he bent, his mouth grazing over the silken skin as he bestowed an erotic supplication to the marks he had inflicted.

Samantha's gasp of outrage was very real as he sought to take an impossible liberty, and she began to struggle, cursing her unspoken acceptance of his actions. 'Don't!' She twisted away from him, struggling in earnest as she fought to escape his plundering mouth, and she began to moan, beseeching him to stop.

For a heartrending moment she thought he wasn't going to listen, then slowly he lifted his head, and his eyes were coolly assessing.

'Why deny yourself an infinite degree of sensual pleasure?'

'Don't you mean salacious degradation?' she choked, and saw his expression assume mocking cynicism.

'Only an innocent would protest so vehemently,' he drawled, his dark eyes agleam with sardonic amusement, and Samantha glared at him with utter loathing.

'How often do I have to put up with this—this——' the words seemed to fail her, then she flung bitterly—'abuse?'.

A dark eyebrow quirked and his lips thinned slightly. 'Be careful with your rash use of words, my sweet wife,' he warned.

'What else would you call it?' she cried defiantly.

Alex examined her stormy expression for endless seconds, then he lowered his head to her breast, seeking with unerring accuracy a rose-tipped peak, circling it with his tongue before taking it into his mouth to taste.

Samantha felt her body go rigid with shock, then she reached for his head, her hands plunging into the thickness of his hair as she tried to pull him away. 'Your barbaric *beast*!' She began to beat his shoulders, balling her hands into fists, and when that didn't succeed, she reached for his hair again and relentlessly tore at it.

'Stop—oh God—*please*!' she whispered in anguish, and sobbed out loud as he lifted his head fractionally, then his mouth shifted to cover hers, his lips hard and compelling as he invaded the inner softness in a savage plundering ravishment.

Then his body shifted to trap hers, his knees applying pressure to part her thighs, and even as she writhed with feverish intensity he achieved his objective with one single powerful thrust.

He didn't move, and his lips took on a gentle persuasive quality as he tasted blood from where he had heartlessly ground her soft mouth. Taking his time, he savoured the warmth with an evocative lingering exploration.

Slowly her resistance melted, and of their own volition her arms lifted to encircle his neck, her hands linking together to hold fast his head. A lambent warmth began to heat her body, sending the blood coursing through her veins like quicksilver, until she was aware of every pulsing nerve centre.

With a sense of growing wonder she felt him swell inside her, then he began to move, slowly and with infinite gentleness until she became caught up in his possession, tossed high on to a plateau of sensual ecstasy so intense she clung to him unashamedly, crying out his name as wave after wave of wild physical sensation consumed her.

Afterwards she lay still, unable to muster so much as a word. Beneath Alex's sensual mastery she had become totally wanton, and that fact filled her with bitter shame. How was it possible to hate and despise someone, yet react in such an abandoned fashion? It didn't make sense.

Perhaps if she closed her eyes she could shut out the emotional complexities which threatened to assume overwhelming proportion.

'Get up,' Alex drawled softly, and her eyes flew wide as she turned to face him.

It was a mistake, for he was dangerously close; close enough for her to see the finely-etched lines spreading out from the corners of his eyes. No man should have lashes that thick, she decided, caught up with the fascination of just looking at him. The well-cut mouth was curved into a slight smile that was wholly sensual, yet it could thin into uncompromising hardness without any effort at all. Dark brown eyes met hers, deep and unfathomable, his thoughts successfully masked.

'We've an hour to shower, breakfast and catch a plane,' Alex murmured, his eyes gleaming with amusement at her surprise.

'Where are we going?'

'Queensland's Gold Coast,' he drawled. 'It's less than an hour away, and at this time of year will be pleasantly warm.'

'Why?' she queried starkly.

One eyebrow slanted, and his expression hardened. 'We could always stay here.'

Faced with that choice, Samantha slipped hastily out from the bed, and his husky chuckle

incensed her to such a degree that she picked up
her pillow and threw it at him.

He fielded it easily, then moved from the bed,
his expression assuming threatening laughter. 'So
you want to play, hmm?'

Samantha ran towards the bathroom with
lightning speed, and on reaching it, closed the
door behind her. Her breasts heaved, her breathing
coming in ragged gasps as she leaned against the
door, expecting any minute for him to push it
open.

But he didn't, and after a few timeless minutes
she moved towards the shower, thankful for the
reprieve.

CHAPTER SIX

EXPECTING to board a commercial flight, Samantha fought to contain her surprise as Alex led her towards a sleek Lear jet parked on an apron of asphalt well away from the main passenger terminal.

A symbol of wealth, it merely served to magnify the formidable hold Alex held over her. No man, regardless of his personal traits, could achieve such success without possessing acute business acumen.

Alex Nicholaos had it all, she thought wearily as the jet received runway clearance and began its swift screaming run before lifting effortlessly into the air, soaring quickly into a prearranged flight pattern.

Well, not quite *all*, she corrected silently. He had a wife; he wanted a son. The two were synonymous, and it was only a matter of time, unless she cared to ward off the inevitable by taking birth control pills. But to what end? If she did bear a child and it was a son, Alex might be magnanimous enough to set her free. Money could buy the services of a competent nanny, and there was Serafina, who would doubtlessly care for the child as if he was one of her own.

'You're very quiet,' Alex's voice intruded, and she turned slightly, taking in the rough-chiselled features, the hidden strength apparent, and she responded civilly,

'I'm not a particularly talkative person.'

'Ah, a dedicated student with little time for the

social graces, eh?'

Samantha sent him a stunning smile. 'Oh, I'm sure you're aware of every little thing about me,' she returned dryly. 'Sophie undoubtedly kept you well informed.'

'That irks you?'

'Unbearably.'

'Poor Samantha,' he drawled, lifting a hand to trail gentle fingers across her cheek.

'I suppose you have a dossier,' she brooded. 'How many times I visited the dentist, the doctor; a list of my academic achievements; who I dated. Have I no secrets?'

'Don't let it bother you.'

'But it does!' she burst out angrily, and to her utter amazement he leaned forward and kissed her with cool hard lips.

'Forget it.'

After that she lapsed into silence and didn't offer so much as a word for what remained of the flight.

A hired car waited for them just outside the Coolangatta air terminal, and Alex stowed their bags, then slipped in behind the wheel.

The Gold Coast resembled a tropical paradise with translucent blue waters crashing down in spuming magnificence on to a wide foreshore lined with tall high-rise apartment buildings.

Their apartment was situated on the top floor of a luxurious multi-storied complex facing the ocean. A panoramic vista was visible in every direction. From Paradise Point in the north, to Burleigh Heads in the south, lay one long curving mass of creamy sand and sparkling sea, and facing inland to the west were the many islands and canals linked together by the meandering Nerang river. Beyond lay the mountains, their rugged terrain appearing a deep indigo blue against the pale azure sky.

The apartment was large, comprising no less than three bedrooms, two bathrooms, a large lounge, separate dining room and modern kitchen, as well as a utility room. Furnished in lacquered cane, the decor relied on various hues of pink and green as a contrast. The overall effect was one of cool elegance.

'It's beautiful,' Samantha murmured with appreciative sincerity.

'The family use it from time to time,' Alex acknowledged and she tried to hide her surprise.

'And it stands empty in between?'

His smile held sardonic amusement. 'It isn't always easy to obtain good short-term tenants.'

The problems of the very rich, she thought silently, sending him a quick glance from beneath her long-fringed lashes. 'How long are we staying?' she asked.

'Two days. I have to be back in Sydney for a meeting on Monday afternoon.'

'The wheels of big business,' she mocked lightly, and saw his lips twist to form a wry smile.

'It can be time-consuming.'

'It can't be time-consuming enough for my liking.'

'The less you have to see of me, the better, eh?' Alex drawled, and she vowed tightly,

'My one hope is that I become pregnant as quickly as possible, then you'll leave me alone.'

He reached out and took hold of her chin, lifting it so she had little option but to look at him. 'Routine tests proved you were a healthy fertile young woman. It shouldn't take long.'

For a moment the importance of his words refused to sink in, then a remembered sequence of events flashed into her mind with vivid clarity. A visit to a gynaecologist earlier that year; Sophie insisting that a specialist, rather than their usual doctor, be consulted for a strictly routine examination.

'You *bastard*!' Samantha whispered, aghast. 'You had it all planned, even then?'

His eyes were hard and totally merciless. 'It was only a matter of time.'

'So you cold-bloodedly covered all the angles.' She was almost speechless with a deep burning rage.

'I had already expended a large amount of money. I merely ensured I received something in return.'

'You're despicable!' Her words were clear and precise, and the look she gave him held bitter venom.

'Do you think me fool enough not to have checked out every detail?' Alex queried dryly.

'It would serve you right if I took steps to prevent conception,' she flung darkly, and his gaze became assessingly analytical as it rested on her stormy features.

'I doubt you'll have the opportunity,' he drawled. 'These next few days are particularly——' he paused, then continued with deliberate emphasis—'significant, shall we say?'

Samantha felt her eyes widen, then narrow slightly with speculative calculation. For a moment she almost stopped breathing, then cold anger took over. Without thought her hand moved in a swift arc to strike a stinging blow to his jaw.

His only visible sign of anger was the dark glitter apparent in his eyes, and she stood transfixed with horror as she saw the darkening patch where her palm had connected. She wanted to run and hide, but there was nowhere she could go that he wouldn't find her.

'You were aware of all the facts before our marriage,' Alex reminded her with dangerous softness. 'Why display such outrage now?'

Because you're too much! she wanted to scream with impotent rage. You, this charade of a marriage—*everything*!

Her gaze became trapped by his, enmeshed, as she fought a silent war against the words she longed to fling at him. Defiance emanated from every line of her body, entwined with a terrible sense of fear. He was angry enough to exact retribution, and she had no doubt as to what form it would take.

After an immeasurable silence he directed harshly, 'Go and change.'

Samantha's eyes widened as she looked at him in askance.

'We're going out for the day.' His wry smile held no humour at all. 'Unless you'd prefer to stay here?'

His implication was plain, and she needed no second bidding.

On reflection the day was not without enjoyment as Alex pointed out the obvious tourist attractions available, then after a pleasant lunch at a picturesque restaurant overlooking the harbour they boarded a cruise-boat for a tour of the Nerang river and canals. There was time for a leisurely walk through the main town centre before making for their apartment, whereupon Samantha declared a desire to swim in the indoor pool situated on the ground floor.

She changed swiftly, slipping a short towelling beach-robe over her bikini, then gathering up a towel she moved into the lounge.

'I think I'll join you,' murmured Alex, his eyes narrowing faintly as they travelled over the slim expanse of her legs, and she felt a surge of latent anger.

'What can possibly happen to me?'

'You are my wife,' he said imperturbably. 'As such you're entitled to my protection.'

She didn't believe any of this! 'Protection from what?' she demanded with incredulity. 'A few possible guests using the pool?'

His smile was humourless. 'I'm an influential man, and because of my interests, newsworthy.' Dark brown eyes held hers with compelling implacability. 'Photographs of our wedding made it into more than one State newspaper.'

'What are you trying to say?'

Alex was silent for a few timeless seconds, then he offered slowly, 'Merely that there are a few disruptive opportunists known for their delight in opposing me.'

Her eyes flicked up to meet his. 'I think you're relating to the wrong country. This is Australia, not America.'

'It's a world of increasing violence—even here.'

'And because of my new status within the Nicolaos clan, I could be a target of some sort?' Samantha queried in disbelief.

'Not in a physical sense,' Alex drawled. 'But imagine the field day the press would have if you were photographed cavorting in the pool with a few nameless young men, and I was nowhere in sight? On what, to all intents and purposes, is our honeymoon?'

'I'm not the type to cavort, as you put it,' she said quietly, 'with strange men.'

'My dear Samantha, you wouldn't necessarily be aware what was happening until it was too late,' he remarked cynically.

She drew a deep breath, then sent him a speaking glance. 'I'm not particularly inclined to provide you with unswerving loyalty.'

His expression assumed sardonic amusement. 'Wait while I change.'

It wasn't the same, she decided hollowly. The half-hour she had sought to spend alone was dominated by Alex's presence. Just the fact that he was there irked her unbearably, despite what he had revealed. Three other guests occupied the pool, and there wasn't evidence of a camera in sight.

They dined at an exclusive seafood restaurant, then took in a floorshow at a nearby nightclub. Samantha had taken extra care with her appearance, choosing a cleverly-cut pant-suit in black silk. Teamed with high-heeled black shoes, and gold chains at her neck and wrist, the outfit was startling and drew more attention than she wanted.

Alex wore conventional formal attire, although the impeccable cut of his suit put him in a class of his own. Many attempted to cultivate that elusive magnetism, but few men possessed it to any great degree.

The short walk back to their apartment block was achieved in silence, and inside the elevator Samantha kept her gaze firmly fixed on the electronic doors, willing them to open before she betrayed the strange tingling sensation racing through her veins. Even her breathing was behaving in an erratic fashion, making her aware of every breath she took.

Inside the apartment she made for the large expanse of glass at the far end of the lounge and stood there taking in the panoramic view. The river looked like a silver ribbon beneath the star-studded velvet sky, and the delicate tracery of street lights resembled minuscule diamonds seen from this height.

Alex hadn't bothered to switch on the light, and she sensed rather than heard him move to stand behind her.

'It looks so peaceful.' There was a strange wistful sound in her voice, and she felt his warm breath tease a few stray tendrils of hair at her temple as he drew her back against him. His arms slid round her waist, one hand slipping down to rest on her flat stomach, while the other sought the creamy smoothness of her breast.

A shaft of exquisite pleasure exploded inside her as his mouth settled on the delicate curve of her neck, his tongue an erotic instrument as he traced the throbbing pulse there before gently nudging her hair aside to render a similar treatment to her sensitive nape.

His fingers splayed out over her stomach, creating a featherlight pattern that unfurled a multitude of sensations from deep inside. Her breast responded to his touch of its own volition, its tender peak swelling with pulsing desire, and she caught her breath as he sought its twin and began a teasing assault on that hardening peak.

Her mind demanded that she tell him to stop, but her body was its own traitorous mistress, brought vibrantly alive by his touch.

She closed her eyes and tried to shut out the conflict of her warring emotions, then a small sigh escaped her lips as she allowed her senses to take over, exulting in the slow rapturous stimulation until a fierce hunger arose, demanding release.

Somehow her clothes, his, were no longer a barrier, and she was dimly aware of being carried,

her arms curled round his neck, her mouth locked
in possession with his.

Nothing else mattered as she became caught up
with desire, so that the need to please as she was
being pleasured broke down the barriers of her
inhibitions.

Her hesitant explorative touch became bold
beneath his guidance, heightening a mutual
arousal so exquisite that she became a willing
supplicant, meeting his demands until every nerve
in her body screamed for his possession.

Their lovemaking held a wild passionate quality
that soared high and scaled impossible unhitherto
reached heights, yet even in its wildness there was
an incredible beauty, the joy of two spirits in
perfect accord.

Afterwards they slept, her body imprisoned close
against his, and even in sleep his hold was iron-hard
and possessive, retaining the merest hint of cruelty.

Samantha woke to feel the touch of lips
tantalising her own, their fleeting softness tracing
the outline of her mouth, tasting the fullness of her
lower lip, then making slow gentle forays to
savour the moist sweetness inside.

Her lashes trembled, then slowly fluttered open
to meet the teasing warmth evident in the dark
brown eyes mere inches from her own.

'Good morning,' Alex said softly.

Her eyes widened slightly as she took in his
vital, *vibrant* features, and a slow tide of colour
crept over her cheeks. She felt her lips tremble, and
there was nothing she could do to hide the
haunting vulnerability evident before her eyes slid
away from his.

'Don't look like that.' His voice was suddenly
harsh, but there was no power on earth that could
let her voluntarily meet his gaze.

She ached all over, even lying supine on the comfort of the bed she was aware of the physical torment created by his excessive demands.

'Samantha.'

For a moment she thought he would force her to look at him, and she couldn't bear having him lay bare her soul. 'I'd like to have a shower.'

Gingerly she edged to the side of the bed, expecting any second to feel his hands haul her back, but mercifully she was permitted to escape.

The stream of water had a warm soothing effect, and towelled dry, her toilette completed, she emerged into the bedroom to see Alex had similarly showered and was in the process of tucking a shirt into the waistband of his trousers.

Crossing to the wardrobe, Samantha selected clean underwear and pulled a dress off a hanger at random, then quickly dressed.

'Would you prefer to have breakfast here, or go out?'

Samantha paused in the action of brushing her hair, and her voice shook slightly as she responded, 'Can we go out?' The thought of being among people held definite appeal.

Alex inclined his head, his expression inscrutable as she smoothed moisturiser on to her face, then applied a light dusting of powder and added a touch of colour to her lips before crossing the room to precede him from the apartment.

They patronised a small French café which specialised in continental breakfasts, and ate an appetising meal outdoors at one of the umbrella-topped tables, basking in the soft warmth of tropical winter sunshine.

Given the choice of a drive into the hinterland, then motoring north to the Sunshine Coast encompassing Noosa and Caloundra, or taking in

two theme parks, Samantha elected to visit Sea
World and Andalucia Park.

It meant mingling with crowds of fellow
tourists, and that was infinitely preferable to being
exclusively alone with Alex.

Watching the trained antics of numerous
dolphins provided light relief and some laughter,
and in the afternoon they viewed the show of
dancing stallions, then wandered round the birdlife
reserve.

Throughout the day Samantha was frighteningly
aware of the man at her side, the slight touch of
his hand, the faint smile he directed on occasion.
Whereas she felt like an automaton, her responses
to his conversation frequently monosyllabic, her
smile automatic. How could he appear so cool, so
unaffected? Did other participants lose themselves
so thoroughly in the sexual act? It was physical
lust at best—or worst, she conceded hollowly.

They returned to their apartment to shower and
change, then dined at a nearby restaurant. She
allowed Alex to refill her glass with an excellent
white wine, sipping it as it went ever so slowly to
her head, making her feel light and floaty, almost
sleepy. It helped dull her aching body, as well as
the deep-seated ache in the region of her heart.

'Let's go.'

Samantha glanced across the table and was
unable to still the faint alarm that sprang into her
eyes before she successfully masked it. His own
hardened fractionally, and the hand that took hold
of her elbow as they strolled back to the apartment
held a hint of steel.

Upstairs she moved slowly into the bedroom,
too enervated to contrive an excuse to delay the
inevitable. Dully she registered the sounds as Alex
locked the outer door, then switched off the lights

until the only illumination came from the lamp beside the bed.

Somehow the bed itself held a mesmeric fascination, and she stood gazing at the silken coverlet, too tired to even begin undressing.

A hand on her shoulder sent the butterflies in her stomach somersaulting crazily, and she made no demur as he slowly turned her to face him.

'I'm tired.' Did she utter those dispirited words?

'And shy,' Alex drawled evenly, tilting her chin slightly, and his eyes narrowed at the dark smudges beneath her lowered lashes, the faint pallor of her skin.

Gently he reached for the zip fastening at the back of her dress, releasing it, then he eased the garment from her shoulders and let it slither to the floor. Next came her slip, then his fingers unclasped her bra.

'Don't—please.' Her voice sounded almost cracked, and he taunted gently,

'Don't—*what*?'

The words seemed to be locked in her throat, and finally emerged as a strangled whisper. 'Possess me.' She couldn't call it anything else. 'I don't think I could bear it.'

'Then kiss me,' he bade, 'and I'll put you to bed.'

Her eyes flickered wide, their depths curiously haunted. Could she trust him? Did it matter? she decided wearily. She had neither the strength nor the inclination to oppose him.

Slowly she reached up and brushed her lips against the clean hard lines of his mouth, their softness trembling slightly as she lowered her head.

Then her chin was firmly lifted and his mouth was on hers, soft and infinitely gentle as he followed the soft curve with his own.

Two huge tears welled and slowly spilled, running down each cheek, and Alex swore softly beneath his breath before tracing each rivulet with his tongue.

She closed her eyes, then felt him lift and place her down on to the bed. The covers fell into place, and she turned her face into the pillow, unaware and uncaring that he crossed to the window and stood staring out into the night's darkness long after she fell asleep.

Their return to Sydney sparked unwanted interest, and Samantha felt a sense of unreality as their emergence from the passenger lounge was recorded by flashing bulbs and questions were flung as relentlessly as Alex parried them.

'What will your stand be this afternoon, Mr Nicolaos?'

'That will be made known at the meeting.'

'But you have definite views, surely?' the reporter persisted.

'It isn't pertinent that I reveal them at this time,' Alex said smoothly, his clasp on Samantha's elbow firm as he walked towards the exit.

'You've only been married a few days. Did you cut short your honeymoon? What does your wife think about this latest development?'

'You know I refuse to discuss my private life with the press,' Alex responded in a clipped voice, and the reporter turned towards Samantha.

'Mrs Nicolaos, if there was one word you would use to describe your husband?'

Oh, lord! Instinct warned that if she faltered, she would be torn to shreds. 'Devastating.' Her eyes were remarkably clear, and the smile she offered was nothing less than dazzling.

Flashbulbs temporarily blinded, then they were

out on the pavement and Spiros was there with the car, reaching for the bags Alex held.

Within minutes the Jaguar pulled away from the kerb, quickly speeding up to join the flow of traffic leaving the terminal.

'How was the Coast?'

Samantha caught Spiros' glance in the rearvision mirror as Alex answered,

'Relaxing.'

Is that what he called it? She endeavoured to mask her expression, and centred her attention on the passing scenery.

The Point Piper mansion looked exactly the same, and within minutes of the car drawing to a halt in the driveway the front door opened to reveal Serafina waiting to welcome them home.

Once inside, the housekeeper indicated she had prepared an early lunch, then she disappeared towards the kitchen while Spiros took the few pieces of hand-luggage upstairs.

Alex threw her a piercing glance, then lifted a hand to rake his fingers through his hair. 'I have a few important phone calls to make. Have Serafina fix some coffee.'

It was back to business with a vengeance, Samantha decided ruefully. As a wife, her place was definitely in the bedroom, and a convenient partner with whom to observe the social graces.

She gave a light shrug. 'I'll go upstairs and unpack.'

Lunch was a leisurely meal. Serafina had prepared a tasty vegetable soup, followed by grilled steak and assorted vegetables, with apple crêpes served with a delicate sauce for dessert.

Alex appeared preoccupied, and as soon as they had finished eating he declared his intention to leave for the city.

After he had gone Samantha viewed the inclement weather outdoors and elected to spend the afternoon writing letters. There were a few close friends to whom she'd promised to send postcards while on holiday. *Holiday!* How did she explain that instead of returning west, she was not only staying, but had married a man they'd never heard her mention! It would take some ingenuity to make it sound any way near feasible, and the effort resulted in a waste-basket full of discarded paper from which she had penned two pages she considered remotely satisfactory.

A knock at the door startled her, and she looked up as Serafina entered the room, her normally kind features wreathed with concern.

'There has been an accident—Alex.' Her breath came out in short gasps as she tried to get the facts out as quickly and as lucidly as possible. 'Spiros has the car ready downstairs.'

Samantha felt herself go cold. 'Is he badly hurt?'

The housekeeper shook her head helplessly. 'I cannot tell you. I do not know.'

'How did it happen?' Oh God, he couldn't be dying, could he?

'Spiros received the call a few minutes ago. He was given no details.' Her face began to crumple. 'I am sorry.'

'I'll get my coat,' Samantha said quickly, and upstairs she paused only long enough to slip her feet into shoes, grab a slim-fitting suede coat from its hanger, then gathering up her shoulderbag she ran down to the waiting car.

CHAPTER SEVEN

THE large city hospital looked clinically ascetic, and Samantha shivered as she was escorted from the elevator down a long corridor to a waiting room.

George turned as she entered, and he moved to her side, his hand reaching for her arm as he drew close.

'He's in theatre. It'll be another hour before we know how successful the surgery is.'

'What happened?' She sounded calm, but she didn't feel it. Right at this precise moment, she didn't know *how* she felt!

George's features darkened with controlled anger. 'Some crazy fool with a gun crashed this afternoon's meeting,' he revealed grimly. 'Witnesses verify that random shots were fired. Two hit Alex.'

Oh God. 'Where?'

'Shoulder and chest.'

Suddenly she felt as if she had to sit down.

'Two of the city's best surgeons are working on him now. I've been assured he has every chance.'

'Depending on the extent of internal damage!' She hadn't realised she'd said the words aloud until she heard George agree.

The next hour seemed to pass with excruciating slowness. George brought them both coffee in polystyrene cups from the huge urn near by, and Samantha sipped it, hardly tasting the contents. She supposed they must have talked, but she had little recollection of what was said. After a while she didn't count the number of times she checked the hands on the clock opposite.

One hour became two, and every time the phone rang or a uniformed Sister appeared she glanced up expectantly. Finally the elevator doors swished open and a tall man wearing theatre garb walked towards them, his expression austere.

In a trance she saw George move forward, and she stood to her feet, waiting, her heart in her mouth.

'Mr Nicolaos is in Recovery. Both bullets have been successfully removed. One pierced the bone of the upper left arm near the shoulder joint. The other entered the chest at an angle. Fortunately the damage is not as serious as it could have been.'

'Then he's all right?' demanded George, and received an affirmative nod.

'He'll need to recuperate from surgery, but I anticipate no lasting ill-effects after suitable convalescence.' He paused, glancing first at Samantha, then George. 'As a precaution Mr Nicolaos will be kept overnight in the intensive care ward.'

'Can we see him?'

The surgeon frowned. 'Tonight? He'll be under heavy sedation. I doubt he'll be aware of your presence.' He moved his attention to the wall-clock near by. 'If you insist, I'll arrange for Sister to allow you a few minutes. Shall we say eight o'clock?'

George murmured his thanks, but Samantha seemed to have lost her voice, and she didn't demur as George led her towards the elevator, then to the waiting car.

The Ferrari leapt into life and purred out of the hospital car park, joining the main stream of traffic with leashed control.

'We'll go to Double Bay,' indicated George. 'We can eat there.'

It took a few minutes for it to sink in that he meant his own restaurant, and afterwards she had little recollection of eating more than a few mouthfuls of food, retaining no knowledge of what it was that she forked into her mouth.

George made a few phone calls. She didn't register to whom, although it seemed obvious his mother and Anna would be anxiously awaiting news. And there was Spiros. Possibly others, as well.

It was precisely eight when they followed a brisk competent-looking Sister into the room Alex occupied. Samantha's eyes flew straight to the hospital bed, unable in those first horrifying seconds to relate the strangely inert man hooked up to various electronic monitoring machines as being Alex. He looked so still, his tautly-chiselled features pale and expressionless—almost lifeless.

It was as if he was someone else, she thought numbly as she followed George from the room, and she hardly registered the words he offered in reassurance.

'I'll contact the hospital first thing in the morning, then ring you, okay?'

His solicitous concern almost reduced her to tears, and she didn't trust herself to speak as she slid into the car.

'You heard the surgeon,' said George. 'There's no cause for concern. Tomorrow Alex will have shaken off the effects of the anaesthetic.' He allowed a faint chuckle to escape, then proffered wryly, 'Knowing my brother as I do, he'll rapidly become the most impossible patient the hospital has seen in a long time. They'll be so anxious to be rid of him they'll do everything in their power to speed him along the road to recovery.'

She looked steadily out of the window. An autumn shower, caught up by gusts of wind, lashed briefly before subsiding into intermittent drizzle, and she became fascinated by the windscreen wipers as they swished back and forth across the contoured glass.

'Did they catch the gunman?' she asked.

'Yes.'

The Ferrari swept in between the wide gates bordering Alex's home and drew to a halt outside the main entrance.

Samantha turned towards him slowly. 'Why?'

George appeared to hesitate, then he offered quietly, 'Who knows? There could be any number of reasons. Alex is currently involved in a few controversial issues.' His voice hardened measurably. 'I have no doubt the cause will be discovered.'

She shivered slightly. Omnipotent power was something in which the Nicolaos brothers excelled, its tentacles far-reaching and all-encompassing.

'Thanks for your support.' Her appreciation was genuinely voiced, and she proffered a faint smile as she reached for the door-clasp. 'I'll hear from you in the morning. Goodnight.'

Once indoors she accepted Serafina's concern and relayed details as she knew them, then refusing a nightcap she turned and went upstairs.

The bedroom looked exactly the same, yet somehow it was difficult to relate to its familiarity without Alex's compelling presence.

Samantha crossed the deep-piled carpet and removed the brocade coverlet, then went into the adjoining bathroom. She felt inexplicably bereft, yet she was too enervated to explore the connotations of such a discovery. A leisurely warm shower would do much to relieve some of her inner tension and, she hoped, speed sleep.

Ten minutes later she slipped beneath the sheets of that large bed, then reaching out she snapped off the bedlamp.

The darkness seemed to envelop her, and she closed her eyes, willing sleep to descend and blot out the turmoil of her emotions.

It didn't work. Even counting sheep had little effect. The space behind her curved back seemed to yawn emptily, silently mocking her sole occupancy.

She alternately plumped her pillow and shifted position countless times, until she slid from the bed with a groan of utter despair. What was the matter with her, for heaven's sake? It couldn't merely be the upheaval Alex's accident had wrought.

A sudden convulsive shiver shook her slim form, and she crossed to extract a warm dressing-gown from the wardrobe, then slipped it on.

Perhaps if she had a warm drink. Milk? Coffee would only keep her awake, and she made her way downstairs to the kitchen, entering Serafina's domain with a sense of invading an unknown sanctum. Finding a saucepan in which to heat the milk, she extracted a carton from the fridge and poured in sufficient to fill a mug, then placed the saucepan on the element.

A glance at her watch revealed it to be almost one o'clock, and when the milk was hot enough to drink she sipped it slowly, then rinsed the saucepan and mug and put them to drain on the sinkbench.

She didn't feel in the least sleepy, and with a sigh she moved towards the lounge, selected a magazine and curled into one of the large comfortable armchairs, intent on leafing through the pages until something caught her attention sufficiently to warrant reading.

'Mrs Nicolaos—Samantha!'

The voice penetrated her subconscious at the same time a hand lightly shook her shoulder, and Samantha roused to see Serafina bending over her.

'Oh dear,' she murmured, attempting to sit upright. 'What's the time?'

'Quarter past seven, and Mr George is on the phone,' the housekeeper revealed quickly, and Samantha emitted an audible groan as she stood to her feet.

'Thanks, Serafina.' She crossed to the nearby phone and picked up the receiver. 'Hello, George? How is Alex?'

'They've transferred him to a private room. He assures me he spent a reasonably comfortable night.'

'You've spoken to him?' she queried incredulously, and George's voice sounded vaguely dry.

'He has a phone beside his bed. I had no sooner put the receiver down from making enquiries as to his welfare, when the phone rang and it was Alex himself.'

Samantha suppressed a wry smile. It would take considerably more than mere injury to keep a man like Alex down for long. 'Did the hospital say when he can receive visitors?'

'I'll pick you up at one. Alex's instructions.'

'Thanks,' she responded gratefully. 'I'll be ready.' She replaced the receiver, then went upstairs to shower and change before returning to the kitchen for breakfast.

Afterwards she put a quick call through to Sophie, then returned upstairs to collect a few things she thought Alex might need. Pyjamas? He didn't wear them in bed, but he must possess some, surely? There didn't seem to be any in evidence in the drawers, and uncertainty furrowed her brow.

For a moment she hesitated, then the decision made, she asked Spiros to drive her to a nearby shopping centre, and thirty minutes later she slipped out of the car at Double Bay.

It was lovely to browse among the shops, although having Spiros in attendance was somewhat inhibiting, and she refrained from taking too much time in choosing her purchases, despite his assurance that he was merely there for her benefit. And protection, she added silently, not discounting the possibility that Alex had issued instructions that she shouldn't be permitted out alone. A security measure, or merely a precaution in case she decided to escape?

George was prompt, and a gleam of admiration momentarily lit his dark eyes before it was successfully masked as Samantha ran lightly down the stairs to greet him.

Attired in a slim-fitting grey skirt and jumper, black suede boots and a silk scarf knotted carelessly at her neck, she looked casually elegant, her movements holding a lissome grace that was uncontrived. A warm coat lay over one arm and as she reached the bottom of the stairs George took it from her and held it out for her to slip into, then together they walked out to the car.

'You look lovely.'

Samantha glanced towards him as he sent the Ferrari purring down the driveway, and her smile held a hint of laughter. 'Thank you. As a morale-booster, you're first class!'

'Nervous?' His quick glance was far too

perceptive, and she sobered, her eyes swinging
back to the windscreen as she tried to inject some
lightness into her voice.

'A little,' she admitted. 'It will be a relief to see
Alex. Last night he looked so——' She searched
for an adequate descriptive and found none.

'Helpless?' George offered wryly, and she gave a
nod in acquiescence. 'I doubt he'll relish the
feeling.'

The hospital looked impressively large as
Samantha entered its revered portals and made her
way to the elevator at George's side. This time
they alighted at a different floor and she
experienced a customary sense of trepidation as
she entered Alex's room.

He was sitting up in bed against a nest of
pillows, looking every inch the autocratic patient—
impatient, faintly arrogant, and bearing no
resemblance to the deathly-pale, deeply-sedated
man she had agonised over less than sixteen hours
previously. True, there was a saline drip attached
to one hand, and his left arm lay immobilised in a
sling, his shoulder swathed in bandages.

Conscious of George's presence, she crossed to
the bed and leaned forward to brush her lips
against Alex's cheek, then she straightened. 'How
are you?'

Dark brown eyes pierced hers, and beneath
their scrutiny she summoned a faint shaky smile.
'You gave us an awful fright,' she managed
unevenly.

'I can imagine.' His voice was a cynical drawl,
and she flushed uncomfortably.

'We have all been most concerned,' George
concurred, shooting his brother a sharp glance.

'I—I've brought you a few things,' Samantha
said quietly, and leaning forward she opened the

door of the bedside pedestal, conscious of Alex's observation as she placed everything neatly inside.

'My dear Samantha,' he drawled musingly, 'pyjamas?'

'You'll need them when you start walking around.' If he intended to embarrass her, he succeeded.

'Such wifely solicitude,' he mocked lightly, and determined not to let him needle her, she said,

'Is there anything else you want? I can bring it when I come up tonight.'

'I think you've covered everything.' His eyes gleamed with sardonic humour, and she looked away, thankful when George began relaying business details of little interest to her.

They didn't stay long, and it was a relief to leave.

'He can be a brute at times.'

Samantha gave George a level glance, unsure whether to agree or maintain a neutral silence. 'I imagine he's in considerable pain,' she said at last, and incurred a wry glance.

'He'll eat you alive, if you let him.'

'I don't intend he shall.'

He chuckled, his eyes gleaming with sudden humour. 'You're exactly what my bother needs.'

She flashed him a twisted smile. 'Someone who'll stand up to him?'

'Just be sure you don't get hurt, eh?'

There was no fear of that, but she deemed it wise not to say so.

The evening visit went little better, this time in the company of Spiros, who discreetly waited in the corridor outside after initially enquiring as to his employer's health. Alex looked tired, his features set in lines of pain.

'Is it very bad?' asked Samantha.

'Do you give a damn if it is?'

Her eyes widened slightly, then she lowered her lids, successfully masking her expression. 'I'll fetch the Sister,' she offered quietly. 'She'll give you something for the pain.'

'They do that at four-hourly intervals,' Alex drawled, and she wrinkled her nose at him.

'You're being a bear.'

'Am I, indeed? Perhaps you'd like to change places?'

She bit back a sharp retort and said civilly, 'Men make terrible patients.'

One eyebrow slanted with mocking cynicism. 'And you're an expert?'

She stood to her feet in one fluid movement. 'I think it's time I left. I'll see you tomorrow.'

'Such a short visit? Spiros will be upset.'

'Anna will be here soon,' she relayed evenly. 'With George. Too many visitors at this stage might do more harm than good.'

'Aren't you going to kiss me?'

Her gaze was remarkably direct. 'I don't think you deserve one.'

'Oh, Samantha,' Alex chided sardonically, 'would it be such a hardship?'

Without a word she crossed to the bed, bending forward to place a light kiss on his cheekbone. Except he moved his head and her lips settled on his mouth instead, at the same time his hand slid to her nape, holding her head as he deepened the kiss.

Shock kept her immobile. That, and the fear if she struggled she might hurt him. Then she was free, and her eyes mirrored momentary pain before she managed to mask it. Without a word she turned and walked from the room, and she didn't look back.

Alex was in hospital for three weeks, and Samantha continued to visit each day, alternating afternoon and evening with George and Anna, so that there was always a member of the family present. After the initial first few days there were other visitors, too, men who were close business associates, and women whose association with Alex appeared highly questionable.

Samantha tried to convince herself she couldn't care less if another female fawned all over him, but there was more than one, all utterly gorgeous and looking as if they'd spent the entire day making themselves beautiful. Beside them, she felt young and incredibly unsophisticated.

Alex seemed to take delight in taunting her, although she doubted anyone noticed. His mouth curved into a soft smile whenever he looked her way, but only she saw that it didn't quite reach his eyes, and there were times when his kiss was deliberately cruel.

One afternoon, only a matter of days before he was due to be discharged, George accompanied her, and they arrived late, due, of all things, to a puncture. That his prized Ferrari should develop such a mundane lapse was beyond his comprehension and Samantha teased him unmercifully.

They were still laughing as they entered Alex's room, and the breath almost died in her throat as she caught sight of the icy anger apparent in Alex's gaze. Then it was masked, and George explained how they came to be delayed, ruefully pointing out the grease marks on his jacket.

It didn't help that Lana, perhaps the most beautiful of all Alex's feminine visitors, was already ensconced in a chair pulled close to the bed, and her barbed innuendoes almost brought

Samantha to boiling point.

'Really, darling,' Lana chided gently, giving Samantha a saccharine smile, 'you must let me introduce you to a few of my favourite boutiques.' Her gaze swept over the fashionable jeans and bulky vee-necked jumper Samantha wore, and she effected a faint shudder before seeking Alex's gaze. 'Don't you agree?'

Alex looked vaguely bored, and his mouth assumed a cynical twist. 'I didn't marry Samantha for her taste in clothes.'

Why tonight of all nights had she chosen to be comfortably dressed? Because it was cold outdoors, she reminded herself, and besides, she'd worked out in the basement studio all afternoon, stretching her muscles to their limit, and she had sufficient experience to guard against cramp. The childish part of her was almost inclined to pull up one denim leg and show the ribbed tights she wore underneath, but reason prevailed. Instead, she directed Alex a singularly sweet smile, then widened it considerably as she glanced towards the older woman.

'I think you'll agree that clothes merely package one's—er—natural attributes.'

Score one for Samantha, George silently accorded as he released a husky chuckle, and his eyes were agleam with devilry as they met hers.

Slowly Lana rose to her feet, and stepping towards the bed she leant forward and bestowed a lingering kiss. 'I really must go,' she murmured with seeming regret. 'Take care, darling. We must get together when you've quite recovered.' Straightening, she turned towards George. 'So nice of you to look after Samantha. I'm sure Alex is most—appreciative.'

'I'll see you out, Lana,' said George as his glance encompassed first Samantha and then his brother. 'Alex deserves some time alone with his wife, don't you think?' His gaze returned to Samantha and he smiled gently. 'I'll wait for you by the elevator.' Then bidding Alex a good night's rest, he escorted Lana from the room.

The silence seemed to stretch interminably, and Samantha plunged her hands in to the pockets of her jeans with a nervous gesture. 'She's beautiful,' she said at last.

'To look at,' Alex agreed sardonically, and she reluctantly met his gaze.

'And very sophisticated.'

'Which you are not, hmm?'

That hurt, and she attempted a light shrug. 'It must be obvious.'

'Lana is a social butterfly, intent on flitting from one eligible man to another.'

'And marriage has taken you out of her reach,' she said dryly. 'Or has it?'

His eyes gleamed with latent amusement. 'Come over here and say that.'

'No.'

'Jealous, Samantha?'

'To be that, I'd have to——'

'Like me? Or perhaps harbour some deeper emotion?'

Her eyes swept to meet his, their expression brooding. 'You're nothing if not brutal.'

'George is far more likeable, eh?'

'He possesses a degree of sincerity,' agreed Samantha. 'Something I find totally lacking in you.'

'I'm little more than an unfeeling tyrant,' he shrugged with thinly veiled mockery, and she struggled with her conscience.

'You're Alex Nicolaos,' Samantha said bitterly.

One eyebrow rose fractionally. 'You say that as if you regard me as Lucifer himself.'

The Devil? Perhaps he was.

'Aren't you going to show wifely concern and enquire as to my progress?' Alex mocked.

'George, Anna and I take it in turns to ring the hospital each morning,' she revealed quietly. 'Whoever has rung then reports to the others. The doctors consider you've made a rapid recovery, and,' she continued evenly, 'that you've been remarkably fortunate. Bone damage to your arm could have been severe had the bullet entered the shoulder joint. As it is, you'll experience lingering pain, and some stiffness which will gradually subside with the help of physiotherapy.'

'Doubtless you're disappointed,' drawled Alex, and on glimpsing her uncertainty he added with soft emphasis, 'Had one of those bullets proved fatal, it would have solved everything for you.'

Pain ripped through her body, momentarily robbing her of speech. 'That's a horrible thing to say,' she said shakily.

'But true, nonetheless.'

She had to get out of the room and away from him, otherwise she'd explode. Even as she turned, his hand reached out and closed painfully over her wrist, and she wrenched unsuccessfully to break free of his grasp.

'Let me go!' Her tawny eyes held glittering gold chips of fury as he drew her inexorably close.

'So much anger,' drawled Alex as he leaned slightly towards her. 'Dare I hope you prefer me alive, after all?'

His face was mere inches from her own, and she could see the black irises in his eyes, the thick dark lashes, the forceful thrust of his jaw and the sensual lines of his mouth.

'Leave me alone, Alex,' she begged.

'In a few minutes. But first, indulge me.'

Even as she opened her mouth to protest his own fastened relentlessly on hers, and she was powerless to stop the deep emotive plundering as he took his fill.

When his head lifted she was left pale and shaking, and she deliberately kept her lashes lowered so he couldn't see the tears threatening to spill over.

'Remembering how you feel in my arms is driving me insane,' he muttered harshly, watching as she rubbed her bruised wrist.

Without a word Samantha turned and walked to the door, not even hesitating as he called her back, and his husky expletive rang in her ears as she moved swiftly down the corridor towards the elevators.

As luck would have it, George had seen her coming, and the elevator doors stood open, waiting for them. It was only when they began to descend that she allowed herself to relax, supremely conscious of George's speculative scrutiny all the way down to the ground floor.

'What the hell happened?' demanded George.

Samantha closed her eyes, then slowly opened them. 'Nothing.'

The soft oath he released was no less intense than his brother's. 'You mean you won't tell me.'

They had reached the car, and as George unlocked her door she slid wearily into the seat and reached mechanically for the seatbelt.

'Samantha?'

'Please—just take me home.'

The engine fired with a growling roar, then

eased out from its parking space and purred towards the exit.

'I'll have Alex's damn hide,' he muttered darkly, shooting her a probing glance as he waited for the lights to change. Then the car shot forward with muted speed, and she was spared having to comment as George concentrated on the busy late afternoon traffic.

Ten minutes later the Ferrari slid to a halt in the driveway, and Samantha made to slip from her seat.

'Thanks for taking me.' Her voice sounded a mechanical imitation, and she shut the door, then walked towards the front entrance.

Inside, she made straight for the lounge, and when Serafina brought coffee she crossed to the drinks cabinet and added a measure of brandy in the hope that the laced brew might steady her nerves. She felt so angry she wanted to hit out and hurt someone. *God!* How could she go on like this! Yet what was the alternative? Leave? A hollow laugh bubbled up inside her throat. She could, but how long would it be before Alex found her? The consequences would far outweigh any benefit.

The intercom buzzed, and she crossed to answer it. 'Yes?'

'Mr George is on the phone,' Spiros relayed calmly. 'Will you take it there?'

'I—tell him I'm busy.' The thought of talking to anyone filled her with antipathy. 'I'll call him later.'

She released the switch, then moved towards the television. There had to be something on that would hold her interest, surely? Two channels were relaying children's programmes, another a documentary, and she settled back to view a Disney animation with little enthusiasm.

Half an hour later Serafina told her Alex was on the phone, and Samantha felt a customary tightening in the region of her stomach.

'Take a message,' she said dully, then, conscious of the older woman's shock, she tempered it with a slight smile. 'He probably wants something taken up tonight.'

Minutes later the housekeeper re-entered the lounge. 'Mr Alex insists on speaking to you.'

'No.' Amazing she could sound so calm. 'You can tell him I refuse.'

'Do you think that's wise?' Serafina queried with a worried frown, and Samantha shook her head.

Wisdom had nothing to do with it. 'We had a—difference of opinion,' she managed quietly. 'You can give him any reason you like. I could be in the sauna, taking a shower—anything. Even tell him the truth. I don't care.'

Serafina started to speak, then obviously thought better of it, for she turned and left the room.

Damn Alex. *Damn* him, Samantha cursed angrily, resolutely attempting to keep her attention fixed on the flickering screen. After half an hour she rose and switched off the set, then made her way upstairs to wash and change for dinner. Not that she felt like eating, she decided wearily.

However, she ate the soup, toyed with the tender slivers of veal, forked a few vegetables into her mouth, and declined dessert.

Serafina's silent disapproval did little to help, and at seven Samantha adjourned to the lounge to view television. An hour later she couldn't stand the tension any longer, and she moved to the phone, pressing the required digits before she had time to change her mind.

The girl on the hospital switchboard put the call through, but it rang unanswered.

'I'll try again.'

Still no answer, and Samantha agreed to hold when the girl offered to make enquiries. It seemed ages before she came back on the line.

'Mr Nicolaos has checked out.'

Checked out? He couldn't have. 'He isn't due to be discharged until Tuesday.'

There was an infinitesimal silence, then the operator revealed cautiously, 'I understand Mr Nicolaos exerted sufficient pressure to warrant an early discharge.'

Oh God. He could be on his way home now. Samantha felt her stomach begin a series of somersaults, then knot with tension. 'What time did he check out?' she asked.

'I believe it was within the last half hour.'

She clutched hold of the receiver until her knuckles turned white, and her voiced 'thanks' was little more than a whisper.

Why? Surely not because of this afternoon? Or the fact that she had refused to take his call? Calls, she corrected shakily. It seemed too ridiculous to even contemplate.

The sound of voices—Serafina, Spiros, George, *Alex*, brought her thoughts sharply into focus. For a moment she hesitated, then marshalling all her reserves of courage together she walked across the room and was about to reach for the knob when the door swung open to reveal Alex in its aperture.

Her eyes swept over him, then settled in the vicinity of his right shoulder. 'I rang the hospital a few minutes ago,' she offered nervously. 'They said you'd checked out.'

'Did they, indeed?' he snapped with brooding intolerance, and she looked at him carefully, unable to control the way her heart lurched at the mere sight of him.

'Don't you think it was foolish to leave ahead of time?'

His eyes held hers with an unwavering scrutiny. 'Why didn't you answer the phone?'

Honesty was the only way to go, and her chin lifted fractionally. 'Because I doubted I could have been civil if I had.'

'You have a valued ally in George,' drawled Alex, his voice faintly cynical. 'He told me in no uncertain terms what he thought of me. He also said you were crying.'

'They were tears of self-pity for having to put up with you!'

His eyes gleamed with sudden humour, then became dark and unfathomable. 'I didn't doubt otherwise.'

The tension in the room could be cut with a proverbial knife, and she rushed into speech, needing to say something—anything, to break the electric silence. 'Shouldn't you sit down? I mean, you aren't even supposed to be out of hospital.' She was aware she was babbling, but she couldn't stop. 'Maybe you should go to bed. I'll tell Serafina to fix up one of the spare rooms.'

'I'm not exactly an invalid,' he said dryly.

'I thought I heard George,' she said quickly, and Alex gave a twisted smile.

'He declined to stay.'

Alex at his worst could be formidable, but she had no doubt George could be equally overpowering. In a battle of wills it would be hard to guess the victor, she decided wryly.

'I'll get Serafina to bring some coffee.'

'Not for me. It will only keep me awake.'

Her eyes swept up to meet his, seeing the faint

edge of strain evident, the rugged features paler than usual. His left arm was confined in a supporting sling, and his jacket hung loosely from his shoulder.

'I think you should go upstairs,' said Samantha concernedly.

One eyebrow arched slightly. 'Are you going to put me to bed and play nurse?'

He was amused, darn him! Well, two could play at that game. 'It's either me, Serafina, or Spiros. Take your pick.'

'Oh, *you*, Samantha,' Alex mocked. 'No one else will do.'

Her heart skipped a beat, then began to thud. 'Then turn round and walk,' she ordered lightly. 'You've been on your feet for the past ten minutes. If you pass out on me, I haven't a hope in hell of picking you up.'

In the bedroom he slipped off the jacket, then unbuttoned his shirt. When his hand went to the belt on his trousers she hastily averted her eyes.

'You're going to have to help me.'

'Yes, of course.' She moved forward as he sat down on the bed, bending down to undo his shoes and then slipped them off. Next came his socks, and she eased the trousers off each leg in turn before placing them neatly over a nearby chair. 'Do you want any extra pillows?'

'One. You can fetch it while I go to the bathroom.'

By the time she retrieved one from the linen cupboard at the end of the hall and slipped it into a clean slip he was sitting up in bed propped against both pillows.

'Do you need anything to help you sleep?' she asked.

'Two painkillers. They're in that phial.'

Samantha crossed to the pedestal and picked up the small bottle, careful to read the instructions before shaking out two, then she handed them to him and fetched a glass of water.

'Anything else?'

'You.'

Her eyes flew open wide. 'You can't be serious,' she whispered shakily, and he gave a rueful grimace.

'Perhaps not.'

It took considerable courage to meet his gaze, but she managed it. 'If you have everything you need, I'll go to bed.'

'Where do you imagine you're sleeping?' he demanded silkily, and her eyes slithered towards his injured arm.

'Across the hall. I'll leave both doors open. If you call, I'll be able to hear you.'

'The hell you are!'

'I beg your pardon?'

'You heard,' he said with dangerous softness. 'The bed is big enough.'

'What about your arm?' she asked steadily.

'Left arm, left side of the bed,' he mocked, and effecting a faint shrug, Samantha made for the bathroom.

A shower did much to restore her composure, and she took her time in the hope that when she emerged Alex would be asleep.

Samantha moved cautiously into the room and all but tiptoed to his side of the bed to switch off the bedside lamp. He had rearranged the pillows for the utmost comfort and lay with his eyes closed. She let her eyes rove over his face at will, and it was all she could do not to audibly catch her breath at the sight of him. Just looking at him unleashed a whole tumult of emotions, none of

which she wanted to explore in depth. There were
questions demanding answers, but she doubted he
would give any.

As her hand reached for the switch his eyes
flickered open and he smiled, a strangely gentle
gesture that softened the harsh planes of his face.

Slowly he lifted his right hand and caught hold
of a handful of her hair, tugging it so she had to
bend down towards him.

'Alex——'

'You smell beautiful,' he murmured lazily. 'I'd
like to taste every inch of you.'

Her mouth was within touching distance of his
own, and she swallowed convulsively, wanting to
end this flagrant seduction *now*, before it was too
late.

'You should be asleep,' she reproved, trying to
break free without much success. To stay like this
was madness.

His lips twisted fractionally. 'Soon. But first——'
He brought her mouth down to his, and his hand
slid to her nape, holding her head fast as he kissed
her.

For a few seconds she resisted, then as he
allowed her to draw back she felt oddly bereft. She
couldn't look away, her eyes becoming locked to
his, and without thought she ran the tip of her
tongue over her lower lip.

His eyes narrowed faintly, then in an unbidden
gesture she slowly lowered her head, her lips
trembling as they came into contact with his, and
she heard his sharp intake of breath.

'What is this? An invitation?'

Pain clouded her eyes, and her mouth shook as
she attempted to break free.

'For God's sake, don't look like that,' Alex
groaned huskily, then he swore with explicit force

as he caught sight of the tears welling behind her eyes. 'Come here, you little fool.'

He brought her head down to his and kissed her, thoroughly.

'Now get into bed, and sleep—if you can,' he added wryly.

Samantha looked at him, her eyes wide and luminous at the depth of emotion evident in that dark brooding gaze. Then she reached out, switched off the light, and crossed round to slip into bed.

CHAPTER EIGHT

ALEX'S convalescence was virtually non-existent. Within days of discharging himself from hospital he had picked up the threads of business, and much against medical advice, began closeting himself in the study for several hours each day.

Rebecca became a regular visitor to the house, arriving before nine each morning to collect dictation tapes. Initially her visits were fleeting, but as the week neared its end she seemed to have found various reasons to prolong her stay.

Samantha found it irked her unbearably. So much so, that she confronted Alex over breakfast Friday morning.

'Can't Spiros drop those tapes into the office each day?' she asked.

He drained the last of his coffee and replaced the cup down on to its saucer. 'He could. However, Rebecca passes this way every morning en route to the office. It's relatively simple for her to call in.' His dark gaze became deceptively indolent. 'Why, Samantha?'

Because she positively *drools* every time she looks at you, Samantha longed to cry out. She didn't, of course. Instead she offered evenly, 'Surely I could help in some way?'

A smile lurked near the corners of his mouth. 'Ah, but you do,' he murmured softly.

His meaning was unmistakable, and her eyes sparked alive with anger. 'Everyone for their specific use, Alex?'

'There was never any doubt about your particular role.'

'No,' she said tightly, hating his musing cynicism.

'Pour me another coffee, there's a good girl. Rebecca will be here soon.'

'Pour it yourself!' She stood to her feet in a rush, her eyes stormy with expressive rage. 'You're not helpless!' If she didn't get out of this room she'd give vent to an invidious display of temper.

'My, my,' Alex drawled. 'You are a spitting ball of fury this morning!' His hand caught hold of her arm, halting her escape with galling ease. 'Why, I wonder?'

She daren't tell him the real reason—she intended delaying that piece of pertinent news as long as possible, at least until she had consulted a doctor, and even after having it confirmed she would ensure Alex was the last to know.

'Because you won't listen to medical advice,' she flung at random. 'You employ an entire team of people who should be sufficiently qualified to deal with everything in your absence, yet you relentlessly push yourself, insisting on participating personally.' She paused to draw breath. 'It's ridiculous!'

'Such wifely concern,' he mocked. 'I find it difficult to believe you consider my welfare so important.'

'Everyone is concerned,' she responded indignantly. 'Spiros, Serafina, Anna—George.'

'Ah yes—George. You appear to share a natural empathy with my brother,' he said dryly, and she retorted,

'He's a likeable man.'

'While I am not, hmm?'

One couldn't apply so tame a descriptive, she

reflected wryly. Alex was too powerful, too compelling, to merely *like*. He stirred extreme emotions, some of which were totally unenviable.

There was a discreet knock at the door, then Spiros entered, his features carefully bland. 'Miss Rebecca Collins has arrived. Shall I show her into the study?'

'Yes,' Alex indicated, shooting the older man a wry glance. 'And have Serafina bring in some fresh coffee.'

'For two?'

Alex nodded briefly, then stood to his feet in one fluid movement. His hand slid down to capture her wrist, and she had little option but to walk by his side from the room.

He paused outside the open study door, and Samantha didn't realise his intention until it was too late. His mouth was faintly cruel and infinitely possessive as it fastened over hers, and as an attempt to humiliate, it succeeded admirably.

The desire to retaliate was uppermost, but in full view of Rebecca's interested gaze there was little she could do. Through throbbing lips she proffered a singularly sweet smile, then reached up and trailed her fingers down the hard muscular edge of his jaw.

'Don't work too hard, darling,' she managed in a soft husky voice. 'I'll ring Sophie and ask her to accompany me into the city. I feel inclined to indulge myself in a shopping spree.' Her eyes were totally lacking in guile as she met his gleaming sardonic gaze. 'You don't mind, do you?'

'Not at all. Spiros can drive you.' He caught hold of her hand and lifted it to his mouth, taking time to kiss each finger in turn. 'As long as he's back by ten-thirty. I have to be at the physio-therapy clinic at eleven.'

'Of course.' Her pulse was behaving in a most erratic fashion, a fact which he was damnably aware of. How could he not know, with his finger deliberately stroking the inside of her wrist and his eyes fastened on the telltale hollow at the base of her throat? She swallowed compulsively, then said evenly, 'I'll get a taxi when I've finished.'

His eyes seemed to silently mock her. 'You haven't forgotten we're dining with Mama tonight?'

'No.' She gave her hand a tiny pull, only to have him turn it over, and it was all she could do not to gasp out loud as he buried his mouth in her palm, blatantly opening his mouth in an erotic evocative gesture that made her burn with untenable fury long afterwards.

'Enjoy your day,' he bade with musing tolerance, letting her escape, and she almost ran to the stairs in her hurry to get away from him.

A telephone call to Sophie revealed that she had already made plans for the day, and Samantha replaced the receiver before crossing to the intercom system linking each room throughout the large mansion. She had no qualms about going into the city alone, and she depressed the appropriate button on the instrument panel, then when Spiros answered she requested he have the car ready in half an hour.

Plastic money was a useful invention, Samantha mused wryly, as she utilised Alex's credit card with flagrant disregard. As revenge, it was piteously childish, for she doubted her purchases would cause so much as a ripple of concern when he received the account.

'Samantha! What are you doing here?'

She turned at the sound of a deep male voice, and her face broke into a welcome smile as she encountered George's friendly features.

'Shopping,' she revealed, unabashed by the assortment of brightly-coloured carry-bags she held in each hand.

'Alone?'

'Well, I tried to persuade Sophie to accompany me, but she couldn't,' she explained with a slight shrug. 'So I decided to come anyway.'

His smile deepened as he drew her to one side of the pavement out of the way of the main stream of pedestrians. 'How's that inestimable brother of mine?'

Her mouth moved to form a faint grimace. 'Instead of resting, he's working.'

'Impossible to subdue, eh?' His eyes twinkled, and she found it difficult to suppress a laughing rejoinder.

'Have you had lunch?'

Samantha shook her head. 'No, I was just about to look for a coffee lounge.'

'Share a meal with me,' George insisted firmly. 'I know of a small restaurant near by where the cuisine is excellent.'

What was the harm in having lunch with her brother-in-law? 'I'd love to,' she accepted gratefully.

The restaurant exceeded her expectations, and after sampling two courses she smilingly declined dessert, opting for a glass of mineral water instead of the thick black coffee George ordered.

'Where to, now?' he queried indulgently as she replaced her glass on to the table with a small sigh

'Nowhere in particular,' she answered honestly. 'I thought I might browse through some of the arcades, then get a taxi home.'

'Today's adventure was by way of an escape?'

He was far too perceptive for words, and she

wrinkled her nose at him in a light attempt at humour. 'How did you guess?'

'I know Alex. At the moment he'll be like a bear with a sore head at being even mildly incapacitated.'

'George! Fancy seeing you here.'

Samantha caught the faint narrowing of his eyes an instant before he stood to his feet, and she felt a strange sense of foreboding as she turned to see the owner of that vaguely familiar feminine voice.

'Lana,' George greeted civilly, extending a hand towards Samantha. 'You've met Alex's wife.'

'Yes, of course, darling—at the hospital, remember?' Her eyes travelled from one to the other in ill-disguised speculation. 'I didn't think I'd see you dining together.'

'Lunching, actually,' Samantha corrected evenly, rising to her feet. 'If you'll excuse me? I must be on my way.' She turned towards George. 'Thanks for taking pity on me. Alex will be appreciative.' The latter was in doubt, but her smile was sincere.

'I must leave, too,' declared George, pulling back the cuff of his jacket to glance at his watch, and Lana gave a faint moue of regret.

'I've only just arrived. Surely you have time to share a drink with me before you go?'

Samantha made to leave, and felt a momentary sense of surprise when George took hold of her elbow.

'Another time?' His curt dismissive nod was brief, and without a further word he signed the bill, then led Samantha outside.

'Are you sure you'll be all right?' he asked.

She looked up, startled by the query. 'Of course.'

'I'll see you tonight.' Seeing her slight frown he

smiled. 'I'm dining at home with Mama. Take care. now.'

It was almost four o'clock when she went in search of a taxi. Two hours had been spent in selecting a dress and matching shoes, and she considered the effect well worth the effort. Out of several perfumes tested she had chosen Miss Dior, and she felt well pleased with her day. Meeting George had been an unexpected bonus, although the same couldn't be said for Lana.

Spiros opened the door the instant the taxi drew to a halt, coming out to retrieve most of the carry-bags while she paid the driver, then she followed him inside.

'Where's Alex?' she asked.

'I believe he is upstairs. I'll have Serafina see to these at once.'

Samantha looked at the various bags trying to remember what they contained. 'There's no hurry, Spiros. There's only a few things I'd like now.' The shoes were obvious, and it took only seconds to discover the dress and perfume. 'I'll take these. The rest can be put in one of the spare rooms until tomorrow.'

Upstairs she crossed to the bedroom and once there extracted the dress from its bed of tissue paper and hung it carefully, then removed the shoes from their box. Hmm, she reflected silently, eyeing the elegant lines. That shade of green was her favourite, a light emerald that enhanced the colour of her skin and lent her dark sable hair a burnished sheen.

She was about to select fresh underwear when the bathroom door opened and Alex moved into the room, a towel hitched carelessly about his hips.

'You're back,' he observed dryly, and her eyes widened fractionally.

'Obviously. Otherwise I wouldn't be here.'

His dark glance seemed to sear right through to her soul. 'I trust you enjoyed your lunch?'

Samantha drew in a deep breath, then released it slowly as she held his gaze. 'Lana hasn't wasted any time. She must have rushed to the nearest phone the minute George and I left the restaurant.'

'So you don't deny meeting him?'

'What is this?' she queried lightly. 'An inquisition?'

'I dislike my wife being the subject of gossip,' Alex slanted brusquely, and she shook her head in disbelief.

'I ran into George quite by accident. It was after midday. He asked me if I'd had lunch, and when I said I hadn't, he suggested we have it together.' Her eyes sparked with hurt anger. 'I didn't realise you would object.'

'Was I to be kept oblivious?'

'You didn't give me the opportunity to tell you,' she responded evenly. 'Now, if you'll excuse me, I'd like to shower and change.'

He moved towards her, and reaching out he caught hold of her chin and lifted it. 'That's the truth?'

'*Yes*, damn you!' she choked.

His grip tightened, and she gasped out loud. 'You're hurting me!'

'I'd hurt you a lot more if I thought for one minute you were using George to avenge me in any way,' he grated harshly.

Never in her life had Samantha glimpsed such inimical rage. 'Let me go!'

His head lowered, and the soundless scream remained locked in her throat as his mouth closed over hers, and she swayed beneath the hardness of his lips as they heartlessly punished in a manner that had her moaning helplessly for him to desist.

A hand slid to her nape and his fingers threaded themselves through her hair, uncaring of her delicate scalp, and defeated, she relaxed her jaw so that he gained entry to violate the soft inner tissue of her mouth.

When it was over she could only stand motionless, her eyes clouded with pain, and he released her with a gesture of disgust.

'We have to leave in half an hour,' he told her impassively.

Oh God, how could she go out tonight and pretend nothing had happened? She turned and made her way wearily towards the bathroom, stripping off her clothes with shaky fingers, then she stepped beneath the shower, soaping herself with determined dedication, all the while willing the tears not to fall.

Afterwards she dressed with care, taking more time than usual with her make-up, then she stood back from the mirror and viewed her reflection, conceding with critical detachment that no one looking at her would guess the defiant turmoil of her emotions.

'Ready?'

She looked up and met Alex's inscrutable gaze, then turned to face him. Attired in a dark three-piece superbly-tailored suit and immaculate white linen, he looked ruggedly arresting.

'Shouldn't your arm be resting in its sling?'

One eyebrow slanted with sardonic cynicism, and he drawled hatefully, 'You sound like a nagging wife.'

Samantha gave a helpless shrug and declined to comment. Crossing to the bed, she picked up a slim evening purse, then caught a warm cobwebby wool wrap over her arm and moved towards the door, uncaring whether he followed or not.

In the car she didn't offer so much as a word as Spiros chauffeured them the short distance to Vaucluse, and she stared out of the window ahead, seemingly intent on the dark-enshrouded houses, mentally preparing herself for the evening ahead.

Alex was at his cynical best, smoothly easing the conversation into safe innocuous channels as they shared a drink before dinner, and throughout the leisurely three-course meal there was nothing to give evidence to their former dissent. With George present, as well as Anna and Nick, and Mrs Nicolaos presiding at the head of the table, there was every appearance of its being an affectionate family gathering.

'You look pale, my dear,' Mrs Nicolaos ventured as they moved towards the lounge to drink the thick strong coffee they all seemed to favour after an evening meal. Her eyes were sharp and amazingly alert as they carefully scrutinised Samantha's delicately-boned features.

Alex cast a deep probing glance at his wife, then let his mouth curve into a wry smile. 'I am not the easiest of invalids, Mama. I have snapped and snarled a little too often these past few days, I think.'

His mother made a faint clicking sound with her tongue. 'Shame on you,' she chided. 'She's such a sweet child—far too nice to vent your ill-humour upon.'

He inclined his head in a mocking gesture. 'I stand suitably reproved.' His glance settled on his wife's downbent head, then he leaned forward and brushed his lips against her temple. 'Forgive me, darling?'

Oh, he was playing his part to the hilt! Had they

been alone, she would have been hard pressed not to *hit* him. Instead she turned slowly to meet his dark intent gaze and said sweetly, 'I shall give it careful consideration.'

'Game, set and match to Samantha,' George observed quizzically, while Anna laughed openly.

'Well done! I haven't witnessed my dear brother being put down quite so well in years!'

Alex's teeth snapped white as his mouth widened into a sardonic smile. 'Oh, she does it all the time,' he drawled. 'I find myself conceding defeat more often than I care to admit.'

'Nonsense,' disclaimed Samantha with bewitching frankness. 'I've never won an argument yet.'

His eyes gleamed with devilish humour as he reached out and trailed gentle fingers down her cheek. 'Ah, but the making up is exquisite, is it not?'

A warm rush of colour tinged her cheeks, and she let her lashes fall in an attempt to veil the anger she felt. He was a callous brute, and she was damned if she would stay here and suffer his merciless teasing.

'I think it's time we left,' she voiced steadily, letting her gaze encompass them all. 'Alex still needs to rest, and if I don't insist, he becomes even more of a bear than usual.'

'I'll drive you,' said George urbanely. 'I'm passing that way, and it will save disturbing Spiros.'

Samantha stood to her feet, then bade everyone goodnight before crossing to bestow a gentle kiss to Mrs Nicolaos' brow. 'It was a lovely dinner. Thank you.'

'Come again soon, my dear. I find your company immensely refreshing.'

In the narrow rear confines of the Ferrari

Samantha leaned her head against the sloping roof and closed her eyes, not bothering to open them until George brought the powerful car to a smooth halt in their driveway less than five minutes later.

He declined to come in for a nightcap, and as soon as Alex had unlocked the front door the car accelerated swiftly, its rear lights little more than a distant glow as it reached the gates to sweep out of sight within seconds.

Indoors, she made her way slowly upstairs, conscious of a strange weariness settling on her slim shoulders, and in the bedroom she took off her clothes, putting them away with care before slipping into a nightgown.

'Let me look at you.'

She turned at the sound of Alex's abrupt drawl and lifted her eyes to meet his, but she was unable to glean anything from his expression. 'I'm tired,' she said quietly.

He had removed most of his clothes, and beneath the soft glow of the bedside lamp his body seemed alive with forceful vitality.

Slowly he crossed to stand within touching distance, and she couldn't have moved had her life depended on it. His hands lifted to frame her face, raising it slightly, and immediately her lashes swept down.

'Open your eyes, Samantha.'

Her lips shook slightly, but she didn't obey. 'Whatever it is you're going to do to me, at least get it over and done with,' she whispered shakily. She was close to tears, and so incredibly weary it was almost more than she could bear to stand here like this, akin to a victim awaiting judgment.

His hands slid down her throat, moving to her shoulders as he gently slid aside the straps of her nightgown, and within seconds it slithered to fall on the floor.

Then his head lowered, and she steeled herself against the punishment she felt sure he would mete out. Instead his lips were deliberately evocative, his touch insistently probing as they moved back and forth on hers.

'Open your mouth,' Alex bade quietly, and she shook her head in mute defiance, then gave a soundless gasp as his lips trailed down to caress the pulsating cord at the edge of her neck. Travelling a tantalising path down to her breast, he deliberately outlined its soft contours before seeking one sensitive tautening peak.

A faint moan escaped her lips as his head moved towards its twin, and she was powerless against the deep surge of emotion that rose within, its treacherous warmth spiralling higher and higher until it reached a brilliant orgasmic plateau.

Just when she thought she could stand it no longer, his mouth slid down to her waist, then moved lower to the delicate softness of her stomach. His mouth created an erotic pattern as it trailed towards one hip, then slowly brushed its way towards the other before settling over her navel.

'Are you carrying my child?'

His voice slowly penetrated the drugged-like mists of her mind, and she shuddered helplessly, crossing her arms over her breasts in a strangely protective gesture.

She wanted to scream out against him, *beg* for the release her traitorous body craved, and she began to shake as anger forced its way to the surface. More than anything she wanted to deny her probable conception, and for a moment she almost did. Then reason returned with the knowledge that he would know soon enough.

'Damn you, Alex,' she swore shakily, endeavouring to wrench out of his grasp. 'Does it please you to know your diabolical calculations were correct?'

'Have you seen a doctor?'

She shook her head numbly, hardly aware that he was pulling her back towards the bed until he sat on its edge and trapped her legs with his own, then he buried his head between her breasts, savouring each in turn before gently pulling her down to lie beside him. Then he kissed her with such incredible gentleness she almost cried.

Slowly the passion within began to ignite and take fire, and for the first time his lovemaking held an evocative tenderness as he led her to the peak of sensual fulfilment.

The same week Alex returned to the office, Samantha had her pregnancy medically confirmed. Not that there seemed to be any doubt, and she emerged from the surgery unsure whether to be regretful or pleased at the news.

Maybe in a few weeks she would view everything differently, she mused wryly as Spiros drove her home. Now, all she could think of was that Alex had gained yet another manipulative victory. It seemed so clinical, so calculated, it was impossible for her not to feel deeply resentful.

'When?' demanded Alex within five minutes of arriving home, and Samanta was unable to resist the temptation to taunt,

'Do you need to be told?'

'Don't sulk, it doesn't suit you,' he declared tolerantly, and she closed her eyes in an effort to control her temper.

'March—precisely nine months and two days from the day we were married,' she revealed waspishly, and she became incensed when he crossed the room and bestowed a brief hard kiss on her mouth.

'I have something for you.' He reached into his jacket pocket and extracted a slim jeweller's case.

Samantha took it from his outstretched hand, reluctant to see what it contained. If he wanted to gift her something, his timing was lousy, she conceded silently.

'Open it.'

'I'm not sure I want to.'

Without a word Alex took the case and withdrew a beautiful gold-linked bracelet, each link studded with diamonds. Taking her wrist, he fastened it on, then lifted her hand to his lips.

'What is this, Alex?' she queried with a touch of wryness. 'Appreciation, or compensation for putting me through months of purgatory?'

She had gone too far—she knew it from the frightening degree of anger that tightened his features into an icy mask.

'Be thankful I don't shake you within an inch of your life!'

She wanted to apologise, but no words would come, and without pausing she turned and fled upstairs to her room, shutting the door firmly behind her, expecting any minute to hear him thrust it open and wreak some form of vengeance.

Instead she was left alone, and an hour later Serafina brought up a tray, her solicitous concern almost proving Samantha's undoing. A headache had been the excuse Alex invented as the reason for her absence from the dinner table, and she felt so utterly wretched it was all she could do to eat any of the tastily prepared food reposing beneath various covered dishes.

Afterwards she showered, then she slipped into bed to settle comfortably against the pillows. Only that morning she had browsed among the shelves of a city bookshop and had purchased no fewer than four interesting novels. One of them should prove absorbing. It was only eight o'clock, and if she kept to her normal routine she had merely an hour before drowsiness would descend.

Except two hours later she was still awake. Damn, damn, *damn*.

Sliding out of bed, she caught up a wrap and slipped it on, then belting its ties, she made her way downstairs. The study was empty, as was the lounge, and for a moment she considered Alex might have elected to sleep in one of the spare bedrooms. Then she remembered the basement studio.

The narrow spiral staircase was already lit, and she descended with care. The studio was empty, although the red pilot light over the sauna was on, and she was within a few feet of it when the door opened and Alex strode out.

He held a towel in his hand, but made no attempt to cover his nakedness, and she was unable to tear her eyes away from the muscular ruggedness of his body.

'Is there something wrong?' he asked.

Samantha shook her head in silence, and he cast her a swift encompassing glance.

'It's late. You should be in bed asleep.'

'I couldn't. Sleep, I mean,' she said hesitantly, and she caught her hands together, nervously twisting her fingers as she fought for the right words with which to continue. Unconsciously her eyes shifted to the wide scar on his chest, letting it slide to the deep cleft running towards his shoulder.

'You find them repulsive?' slanted Alex, his eyes narrowing at her apparent absorption, and she shook her head.

'No,' she disclaimed slowly, lifting her gaze to meet his. 'You haven't mentioned when the court case comes up.' She hurried on as one eyebrow rose in cynical query. 'You'll have to testify, won't you?'

'I find it difficult to believe that is responsible for keeping you awake, or for seeking me out at this late hour,' he drawled with a touch of mockery.

Samantha kept her gaze steady with difficulty. 'I came to tell you I'm sorry.' The tip of her tongue edged out and traced along her lower lip, and his mouth twisted as he taunted wryly,

'Are you?'

'Yes,' she said simply. 'It's a beautiful bracelet, and I was perfectly horrid.'

'Spoken like a truly repentant child,' he gibed softly, his eyes agleam with latent amusement. 'What comes next? Are you going to kiss me by way of atonement?'

She swallowed compulsively, suddenly conscious of the way her pulse was behaving. 'If you like.'

He lifted a hand and trailed his fingers down the neckline of her wrap. 'Go back to bed. I'll close everything here first, hmm?'

Slowly she turned and walked from the large room, mounting the two flights of stairs to the uppermost floor, then she went into the bedroom and sat down on the bed.

Five minutes later the door opened and Alex entered the room, a short towelling robe belted at his waist.

Her eyes felt incredibly large as she watched him walk towards her, and her teeth caught at the lower edge of her lip in a gesture of nervousness.

He was a law unto himself, more often cruel than kind, and utterly ruthless on occasion. Yet he had the power to make her respond in a way she had never dreamed possible. Discovering *why* was something she didn't dare explore, sure in the knowledge it could only be soul-destroying to fall in love with a man like Alex.

'Do you need to summon courage to kiss me?'

More than you know, she reflected silently as she stood to her feet. Taking the few steps necessary, she moved to stand in front of him, then reaching up she brushed her lips against his. 'I'm sorry.'

'Sorry for kissing me?' he arched sardonically, and she felt immeasurably hurt.

'You're not making it easy,' she said shakily, and his lips twisted fractionally.

'Are you suggesting I should?'

'Sometimes I think you deliberately try to make things as difficult for me as possible.'

'Not true,' he denied quietly. 'If anything, *you* make it difficult for yourself by refusing to face up to the obvious.'

What was obvious? Samantha felt so confused and at odds with her emotions, it was impossible to think straight.

'I think I'll go to bed,' she said shakily, and he smiled.

'Opting out, Samantha?'

She looked at him askance, and saw the faint teasing gleam in his eyes.

'You can't by any stretch of the imagination call that token gesture a kiss?'

Samantha felt her lower lip tremble slightly.

'Don't play with me, Alex. I don't really think I can compete with you any more.'

'Believe that I have your welfare very much at heart, and I'm loath to hurt you at all.'

Without a word she reached up and wound her arms around his neck, and her mouth opened generously as it touched his. Her exploration was tentative at first, then became increasingly confident as his arms linked about her waist, pulling her close so that she was in no doubt of his arousal. Then gently she eased the robe from his shoulder, and her lips traced a light butterfly path over first one scar, before moving to caress the other.

His husky groan did strange things to her equilibrium, and she stood transfixed by the deep slumbrous ardency of his gaze.

'Don't stop,' he muttered.

As if in a dream she reached for the tie at his waist and released it, then she eased the robe off his powerful shoulders with fingers that shook.

'You're an ardent lover, my sweet Samantha,' he husked gently as he bent and touched his lips to her temple before letting them trail down to her ear. 'Please me, as I have pleasured you.'

And she did, hesitantly at first, until his pleasure became her own, and together they scaled the heights to a degree almost beyond mindless passion, exulting in each other before seeking the ultimate release of total possession.

On the edge of sleep Alex curved her supple young body close in to his, and murmured gently,

'I have to be away for a few weeks. Melbourne, Adelaide, Brisbane, then north to Cairns.'

Samantha felt incredibly drowsy. 'When do you leave?'

His lips brushed the top of her hair, then slid

down to caress her temple. 'The day after tomorrow.'

'Promise me you'll take care,' she whispered, and felt his lips move to form a smile.

'You have my solemn word.'

CHAPTER NINE

THE airport lounge was crowded, and Samantha stood beside Alex as she waited for his flight to be called.

'Alex! Sorry I'm late,' a feminine voice proclaimed breathlessly, and Samantha felt her eyes widen in disbelief as Rebecca came to stand beside him. 'The taxi got caught in a traffic snarl-up that took ages to disperse.' Her eyes became deliberately bland as she greeted Samantha. 'Good morning.'

'You're accompanying Alex?' Why ask the obvious? Yet she had to have confirmation.

'Only to Melbourne,' Alex put in in a clipped voice, his eyes narrowing as they rested on Samantha's expressive features. 'Rebecca is extremely efficient.'

I just bet she is, Samantha thought silently, feeling her heart plummet at the thought of them being together.

At that moment the flight was called, and Alex bent and kissed her briefly, almost dispassionately. 'Try to miss me, eh?' Then he was moving towards the gate.

As soon as he was out of sight she turned towards Spiros and indicated that they should leave.

She didn't say a word on the way home, and looked up in surprise when Spiros indicated that she should follow him through to the kitchen.

Once there, he drew her towards the laundry, and even as she went in there came the most pitiful whimper from a basket near the door.

'For you, Miss Samantha,' Spiros revealed with a broad smile. 'Mr Alex thought it might provide some company during his absence.'

The most beautiful spaniel puppy sat among a pile of makeshift blankets, his brown eyes soulful, his long silky ears flopping softly as he looked from one to the other of them, not sure who he should appeal to for affection.

'He's beautiful!' Samantha breathed, slipping down on to her knees to pick him up. Laughing, she buried her face against his silken fur, then cuddled him unashamedly. 'I'll call you Rufus.' She glanced up at Spiros. 'He doesn't have a name, does he?'

'Mr Alex left that to you.'

The puppy was a joy, and followed her everywhere. He even leapt into the pool in an effort to be close to her, and thereafter paddled a length when she swam each day before whimpering in the shallows to be lifted on to the side, where he raced up and down barking madly until she elected to come out.

The first week passed quickly, the days proving relatively easy to fill. It was the nights that were unbearably lonely, and a bunched pillow beside her was no compensation for the warmth of Alex's body.

She visited Mrs Nicolaos every second day, met Anna for lunch once, and wandered round Taronga Park Zoo with two of Sophie's nieces.

Alex had telephoned twice, and hearing his voice started up a whole host of emotions, some of which were hardly enviable. Part of her longed to ask after Rebecca, but to do so would be unutterably childish, and afterwards she stayed up later than usual viewing television, trying to convince herself the programme held her entire attention.

The next morning Samantha woke feeling as if she could easily have slept another few hours, which was ridiculous considering it was already past eight. A strange lethargy seemed to possess her limbs, and there was a tight ache making itself felt in the small of her back, which she dismissed as having slept awkwardly.

After a shower, she dressed in a comfortable cotton shift, brushed her hair and caught it into a knot on top of her head, then brushed her teeth vigorously before moving back into the bedroom.

This was the third consecutive morning that she had managed to rise without experiencing the stomach-churning nausea that inevitably meant a swift run to the bathroom. Tea and dry biscuits before she set a foot out of bed had helped on the odd occasion, but for the most part she had become resigned to the havoc this child was causing within her.

Now she cautiously considered maybe that part of pregnancy was past. Another milestone, she decided wryly as she moved downstairs. Her waist had definitely thickened, but everywhere else she was still as slim as a reed.

'Morning, Serafina,' she said brightly as she crossed the kitchen and sat down at the table. Her customary glass of chilled orange juice was there in readiness, as well as cereal, with several fruit conserves to spread on her toast.

'It is a beautiful day,' that good woman announced after returning the greeting. 'Have you seen the sunshine?'

'I have. What's more, I intend getting my first tan of the season, then I'll swim in the pool. Alex would approve, don't you think?' This was lightly said, and received a nod in response.

'Have you any plans for the day?'

The thought of going into the city and battling crowds of shoppers didn't appeal. 'No, I'll just stay home and have a lazy time.'

And she did, stretching out on the lounger beside the pool, the brim of her hat shading her face as she alternatively read and dozed for more than an hour before slipping into the pool for a leisurely swim.

The water was pleasantly cool on her limbs, caressing her skin like silk as she executed a neat crawl for two lengths before turning on to her back. For a while she floated aimlessly, then she turned and headed towards the steps.

It was as she emerged from the pool that the pain attacked. A twisting agonising fist seemed to clench inside her stomach, then stabbed like a knife through to her back.

Samantha stood for a few seconds, held motionless by pain, then as quickly as it came, it disappeared.

Perhaps she'd overdone the swimming, but even as the thought occurred, she dismissed it. Nor could it be anything she'd eaten. There was only one logical conclusion, and her heart began to hammer with fear.

A miscarriage? At three months? Her obstetrician seemed delighted with her progress.

For heaven's sake, she chastised in self-admonition as she moved to collect her towel and began drying off the excess moisture. There was probably a perfectly valid reason to explain it. In any case, she was due for her monthly check-up tomorrow.

Indoors, she moved upstairs and had a quick shower, then she dressed and went down for lunch.

As she was about to descend the last step, the pain ripped through her again, more intense this time, and she gripped hold of the banister, then sank down clasping her knees.

'Serafina!'

The sound of running footsteps was reassuring, and it needed little explanation to send that good woman running for Spiros.

What happened next developed a slight haziness, for she had little comprehension of time. Spiros must have phoned for the doctor, for it seemed only minutes before she was being transported by ambulance to the hospital.

Then she was surrounded by medical staff, admitted and put to bed, only to be constantly disturbed as one nurse after another seemed to appear with increasing regularity to monitor her pulse, blood pressure, or simply to ask questions. The doctor arrived, completed his examination, consulted with the Sister-in-charge, then gravely told her it appeared certain she would miscarry.

A strange numbness settled over her like a cloak, protective by its presence in not allowing her to think. She wanted to cry out that she didn't believe what was happening, but as another agonising muscular contraction made itself felt she knew that refusing to face up to the truth was nothing less than folly.

Strangely the sun was still shining, its rays penetrating the glass windows and casting beams on to the vinyl floor.

'Would you like a magazine to read?'

Samantha glanced up and only just refrained from giving an hysterical burst of laughter. Read? She was losing her child, and they wanted to know if she would like to *read*?

The pains began to come more frequently, their intensity savage as her womb moved to eject its rejected foetus.

At five o'clock two nurses wheeled her down the corridor to a waiting elevator, and the sinking sensation in her stomach became synonymous with the descending electronic carriage.

They placed her in a small screened-off ward that was alive with the sound of hospital activity, and the merry-go-round continued, repeating itself with further monitoring and another examination, then mercifully she was left alone.

Then minutes later the screen was pulled aside to reveal none other than Alex, and his tall frame seemed to loom large, filling the small space as he moved towards the bed.

'What are you doing here?' Did she sound that ungrateful? Almost accusing?

'Spiros rang me,' he enlightened her bleakly. 'I caught the next plane back.'

'You can't do anything,' the words seemed wrung out of her, and he said quietly,

'I can be here.'

A fierce spasm of pain racked her body, and she cried out against it, unable in its aftermath to refrain from venting, '*Why?* Can't I even have the privacy to do this alone? *Oh God!*' Nothing had ever hurt this much, not even when she'd fallen out of a tree and broken her arm soon after she'd started junior school.

An unintelligible oath left Alex's lips. 'Where the hell are the nurses, the doctor?' He caught hold of the electric buzzer and held his finger over it until quickened footsteps heralded the presence of the medics required.

'Damn it! Can't you give her something?' His anger was a volatile tangible thing, and within minutes someone in a white coat moved forward, cleansed a patch of skin, then plunged in a syringe which soon provided a floaty disembodied feeling.

The pain was still there, but somehow it didn't have as much impact as before. A drip was attached to her arm, and after that she had a very hazy recollection of what went on.

At some stage she must have drifted off to sleep, for when she woke she was back in her room, the curtains at the window were drawn, and there was no more pain, only a peculiar emptiness.

Slowly she let her eyes encompass the room, and her heart tripped its beat and began to thud as she saw Alex seated in a chair near by.

He wasn't asleep, but his attention seemed elsewhere, and she was able to watch him unobserved, noting the slight sag of those powerful shoulders, the rather grim set to his features. Then she must have moved, for his eyes lifted, alert and infinitely watchful as he trapped hers.

She seemed incapable of speech for what seemed an age, then slowly her voice queried huskily, 'It's over, isn't it?'

He hesitated, then briefly inclined his head. 'Yes.'

Samantha closed her eyes against the potent force he exuded. He couldn't attach any blame to her, could he? A huge lump seemed to grow inside her throat, and twice she attempted to swallow it without success. 'Is it very late?'

'After eleven.'

'Go home, Alex,' she bade, suddenly tired. Wearily she turned her head against the pillow, seeking the reassurance of its softness. Tears filled her eyes, then slowly overflowed to slide down her cheeks. Two more followed, and together they paused, poised on the edge of her chin, then momentum plunged them to run down her neck.

A handkerchief touched her cheek, dabbing

gently at the increasing flow, and it was more than she could bear.

'I'd like to be alone,' she whispered.

She sensed rather than heard his soft oath, then he stood upright.

'I'll have Sister give you something to help you sleep.'

She didn't seem capable of saying a word, and when Sister's quiet voice and the soft rustle of movement roused her, Alex had resumed his seat in the chair near by.

It was still dark when the hustle and bustle of early morning hospital activity penetrated Samantha's subconscious, and she struggled against wakefulness, resenting having it forced upon her.

Five o'clock was an ungodly hour to be roused, and she slipped in and out of sleep until a hovering nurse insisted she rise and take a shower.

Anyone who thought they would come to hospital for a rest was in for a shock, she decided as the day wore on. Doctors' rounds, specialist rounds, tea, not to mention the constantly monitoring nursing staff.

Flowers arrived before lunch. Huge florist-arranged bunches, which were set in vases and displayed to their best advantage within the confines of hospital dictum. The message on the accompanying card was brief, and depending how you viewed it, could have been a genuine gesture, or merely conforming to what was expected of him. In black ink, which seemed oddly appropriate, was scrawled—*Love, Alex*.

Afternoon visiting hours brought Sophie, and her sympathetic affection acted as a soothing balm.

A further floral tribute was delivered late

afternoon, and Samantha was moved to fresh tears when she saw that it came from Serafina and Spiros.

Alex entered the room at seven, and immediately Samantha felt the fine edge of tension creep into her veins. The telltale pulse at the base of her throat began to quicken as he moved to the bed and bent low to brush his lips against her cheek.

'How are you feeling?'

'Better,' she managed quietly, then she gathered sufficient courage and lifted her eyes to meet his. 'Thank you for the flowers.'

His expression was enigmatic, and she suspected he was being deliberately bland as he sat on the edge of the bed.

'Is there anything you need?'

Need? I need what I just lost, she longed to cry out—your child. The knowledge shocked her. Up until now she had purposely not given it much thought. Dazedly she searched his set features and was unable to ascertain anything. Her voice came out as a shaky whisper. 'No.'

There was a moment's silence, then he said, 'The doctor says you can come home the day after tomorrow.'

She had been told much the same thing that afternoon, and she nodded her head. What could she say?

His eyes were sharp and much too discerning, and she let her gaze slide to a point beyond his shoulder.

'Samantha——'

'Don't, Alex—please,' she stumbled shakily. 'I couldn't bear any recriminations just yet.'

His husky oath was audible, and she cringed at the soft force of it. He caught hold of her chin and lifted it high. 'What makes you think there will be any?'

She didn't answer, and as the silence stretched out he gave an impatient sigh.

'What happened was an act of God, or maybe Fate. Who knows?' He lifted a hand and thrust his fingers through his hair, ruffling it into attractive disorder. 'All that is important is for you to get well.'

'Your hope of a child isn't lost for ever,' Samantha told him wretchedly. 'I've been told I'm in good physical childbearing shape.' A faintly hysterical laugh left her lips. 'It's even been suggested I become pregnant again as soon as possible.' Her lashes lowered to veil her eyes as she muttered indistinctly, 'Rather like a rider instructed to mount a horse again after a fall.'

Alex's eyes were dark and glittery with suppressed anger, and with an impatient gesture he stood to his feet and moved to the window. His gaze on the scene beyond that pane of glass seemed to hold his entire attention for an immeasurable length of time, then slowly he turned back towards her.

'Anna will visit tomorrow afternoon.' He thrust his hands into his trouser pockets, and his expression was broodingly inscrutable. 'Mama regrets her inability to move from her house, but has extracted my solemn word to bring you to her for a short time on the way home from hospital. George sends his regards, and has conveyed that he will probably call in tomorrow evening.'

Samantha swallowed unevenly. 'They all sent flowers,' she said quietly. 'Please thank them for me.'

'They've become very fond of you.'

What about you? she longed to scream. Have

you become fond of me, or is it all still a deplorable sham? The need to discover his feelings defeated her. He could be tender and incredibly gentle on occasion, only to change into a formidably pitiless tyrant the next. Trying to unravel her own emotions was bad enough, without attempting to understand *his*.

'How is Rufus?' she queried out loud.

'Missing you.'

That made sense. The lovable mutt was affection on four legs, and incredibly loyal. 'What about your business trip? You weren't supposed to return until tomorrow.'

His dark slanting glance pinned hers. 'My wife ill in hospital is more important than any business interest.'

There didn't seem much to add to that, and she wasn't in the mood to argue. Some things were best taken at face value.

After a while Alex left, and she didn't plead with him to stay. Alex was more than any one woman could handle, and his leashed masculinity seemed to fill the room, a potent force which made her feel incredibly helpless.

Surprisingly she slept right through the night, and woke feeling refreshed and alert. Sophie visited her early in the afternoon, and was followed by Anna and Serafina.

Samantha ate well, and ventured along the corridor for exercise, enjoying the company of other patients in the hospital lounge. She had a shower after dinner, and did the best she could with her face and hair, applying a light dusting of powder and a touch of colour to her cheeks.

Shortly before seven a tall figure walked through the door, a broad smile on his friendly features, and her faint smile widened with pleasure.

'George! It's so good to see you.'

'My word, that's some welcome.' He crossed to the bed and bent low to brush her cheek with his lips, then he straightened and sat down on its edge to regard her teasingly. 'Well now, this is a great way to get attention.' He waved a hand towards the masses of flowers. 'There's hardly room to move.'

Her eyes twinkled and she laughed softly. 'I know. Everyone has been very kind.'

'Everyone?'

She sobered slightly, and her gaze was remarkably steady. 'Yes.'

'Alex tells me you're allowed home tomorrow.'

A nervous flutter made itself felt in the region of her stomach. 'There's no need for me to stay here any longer.'

Kind brown eyes became shrewd and penetrating. 'Look after yourself, little sister-in-law,' he said gently. 'That brother of mine can be something of a brute on occasion.'

Oh heavens, in another minute she'd cry. 'Aren't all men that at times?' she demanded with deliberate lightness, and incurred his wry smile.

'But a certain Greek more often than you care to admit, hmm?'

'I think we should change the subject,' Samantha said evenly.

'You're very loyal.'

'Aren't I supposed to be?'

He moved a hand towards her cheek and trailed gentle fingers down the finely-etched bones until he reached her chin. 'You're a very sweet girl, Samantha. You care about the frail and elderly, young children and animals.' His lips curved into a half-regretful smile. 'It's a pity Alex saw you first.'

'Nevertheless, I did,' a deep voice drawled from

the open doorway, and George merely smiled while Samantha withdrew as if from a threatening flame.

'Ah, you've arrived,' George greeted dryly, and Alex slanted him a probing glance before crossing to the bed.

Samantha cast him a wide-eyed look which held a tinge of guilt, and there was nothing she could do to prevent the faint tremble of her lips as his mouth closed over hers with gentle possession.

As he lifted his head his eyes were dark and unfathomable. 'You look much better.'

'Yes,' she murmured uncertainly.

It was a relief when visiting hours drew to a close. George was the first to leave, his wry smile clearly indicating that he was giving them time together. To do what? she felt like crying out, silently begging him to stay. Yet to feel this way was ridiculous. Sooner or later she had to face Alex alone. Tomorrow, she reminded herself dully.

'I'll be here at ten,' Alex informed her, sitting down on the edge of the bed.

His closeness bothered her, and a betraying pulse began to thud at the base of her throat. She lifted her eyes with a momentary lack of comprehension.

'You can be discharged between ten and eleven,' he reminded her, and a faint tinge of colour crept over her cheeks.

'Spiros could easily collect me,' she offered quietly.

'Is there some reason why I shouldn't bring you home?'

His voice held a hint of arrogance, and something else. Anger?

'No, of course not,' Samantha answered

quickly. 'I just thought it would be less of an inconvenience.'

His nostrils flared briefly, and there was a dangerous glitter in his eyes. 'You think too much.'

She swallowed convulsively. 'Alex——'

'Shut up,' he said tautly, leaning forward, and his lips fastened on hers with a strange gentleness, seeking the inner softness of her mouth with the tip of his tongue.

It was evocative, yet undemanding, and after the initial moment when she had instinctively withdrawn, she began to relax, aware that Alex was in an amenable mood—this time.

As he straightened she felt a strange sense of loss, and her eyes seemed large and luminous as he outlined her mouth with a gentle finger.

'I must go.' His smile did odd things to her equilibrium. 'Sleep well. I'll see you in the morning.' Then he was gone, and she drowsily refused a sedative when Sister made her round almost within minutes of Alex's departure.

The day dawned bright and clear, the sun's warmth embracing everything below as it rose higher in the sky. There was pleasure mixed with reluctance at the thought of returning to the elegant luxury of Alex's Point Piper home. It was almost as if it was symbolic of the reckoning that had to come.

Samantha was dressed and ready, the necessary discharge form signed, when Alex entered her room in the company of the ward Sister and a resident doctor.

Ten minutes later she was comfortably seated in the Mercedes as Alex eased it into the flow of traffic.

'Mama has arranged a light snack.' He spared a

quick sideways glance. 'I've warned her we won't stay long.'

How could she have forgotten? Mrs Nicolaos was a very astute old lady, known for her outspokenness, but she was not lacking in tact. Samantha doubted she would be anything but sympathetic.

And so she was—saying little, but managing to convey without words precisely what was necessary. Her frail arms had closed briefly, but tightly, over Samantha's shoulders before relinquishing her to the care of her son.

They shared delicate sandwiches and iced pastries, together with the sugary dates Mrs Nicolaos so loved, and there was tea as well as the strong thick coffee Samantha usually avoided.

The faithful Helena hovered ever dutifully, tending their needs and those of her mistress, and it was almost twelve when Alex made clear his intention to leave.

Five minutes later they were home, and Samantha bore Serafina's welcoming ministrations with the assurance that she was feeling quite well, adding more for that good woman's benefit than her own that it was nice to be home again.

Rufus was ecstatic, attesting in animal language that he was delighted to see her again, so much so that Alex banished him to the laundry until he calmed down.

'Now, a rest before lunch,' insisted Alex, his eyes narrowing faintly as they took in her pale features, and when she would have protested he lifted her into his arms and carried her upstairs.

In the bedroom he laid her against the pillows, then eased off her shoes.

He seemed disturbingly close, and to shut out

his forceful image Samantha let her lashes flutter down until they closed.

'Is there anything you want?'

She wanted to cry out for him to hold her, but the words never left her throat, and after a moment's hesitation she shook her head.

'I'll come and get you at one.'

A faint sigh left her lips. 'I'm not an invalid.'

'Did I suggest you were?' Alex's voice queried silkily.

Who was she to refuse some tender loving care? God knows she felt badly in need of it! 'I suppose you've taken the day off?'

'Yes.'

For some reason she felt close to tears. 'Thank you.'

'For what?' he demanded tersely. 'Showing an inclination to be with my wife?'

'Do you? Want to be with me, I mean?'

'Samantha, by the living Heaven!' he muttered emotively. 'I could shake you until you *beg*!'

Her lips trembled, and he appeared to make a concentrated effort to control his temper. Biting off a husky oath, he turned abruptly and left the room.

Lunch wasn't exactly a relaxed meal, although Alex seemed to maintain a conversational flow, even if Samantha's answers tended to be monosyllabic, and with Serafina hovering between courses it was impossible for any dissension to occur.

Throughout the afternoon Samantha alternately viewed television, leafed through magazines, even dozed on the sofa for an hour, then inserted a cassette into the video recorder that proved lighthearted and scintillatingly funny.

At six she went upstairs and showered, then, her

toilette complete, she selected a simply-cut dress of soft silk in delicate pastel hues, added slender-heeled shoes, and attended to her make-up. A light dusting of powder over a film of moisturiser, with shadow and mascara to highlight her eyes, a touch of blusher to her cheeks and gloss over her lipstick. Electing to leave her hair loose, she applied the brush with vigorous strokes, then stood back to check the result.

It was the first time she had cast her overall image a glance since going into hospital, and she noted dispassionately that there was little difference. Her outline was as slim as it had ever been, and only the keenest eye could detect a slight shadowy sadness in her expression.

Somehow she managed to get through dinner, although her appetite seemed to be negligible as she endeavoured to do justice to the tempting courses Serafina had prepared.

Afterwards she took tea while Alex elected to drink his usual strong brew.

'Would you like to view television?'

Samantha looked up at the sound of Alex's voice and gave a swift nod. It meant they wouldn't have to talk, and although they must eventually, she far preferred to push it as far away from the present as possible.

At nine she rose to her feet voicing an intention to retire, and Alex extracted his lengthy frame from the chair with indolent grace.

'I'll see you upstairs.'

Her eyes widened fractionally. 'There's no need.'

'Indulge me,' he drawled. 'You were equally solicitous when I emerged from hospital.'

'I've only had a miscarriage.'

Dark eyes riveted her own. 'Something which is an emotionally traumatic experience.'

'What do you want to do, Alex?' she flung with

a trace of bitterness. 'Hold my hand?'

'I'm not so inhuman I can't appreciate something of what you're feeling,' he said quietly. 'It was my child, too.'

She felt the tears fill her eyes, and the thought of having him witness them made her turn and run. Except she had taken only two steps when strong hands closed over her arms and she was lifted struggling into his arms.

'Put me down!' she cried.

'Be still, you little fool!'

In the bedroom he let her slide down to stand before him, his arms linking behind her back to draw her close. It was as if he wanted her to absorb some of his strength, and after a few infinitesimal seconds she simply pressed her face into his shirt and let the tears fall.

The steady beat of his heart beneath her cheek was reassuring, and after a while she drew back.

'Get into bed,' Alex directed. 'I'll go downstairs and close the lights.'

Samantha turned and began to discard her clothes, then she moved into the bathroom. She felt infinitely weary, a combination of mental and physical exhaustion.

When Alex slid into bed she was almost asleep, and she didn't offer any resistance as he drew her into his arms, pillowing her head against the curve of his shoulder in a strangely protective gesture.

CHAPTER TEN

THE next few weeks were unbearable. Samantha seemed locked in a private world not even Alex could penetrate. The medics had an expression for it—post-partum, or post-natal, blues. Except this was worse, because she was consumed with guilt over the loss of the child.

Not that she was in any way responsible, but because she hadn't really welcomed its conception in the first place. It hadn't even been her decision. Alex was master in control of all the strings, she merely the puppet. It wasn't as if she didn't love children, or eventually want some of her own. Somehow she had associated having them as a result of an all-consuming love she would share with their father. And it hadn't been like that. Part of her was resentful at having had motherhood thrust upon her, another raw and bleeding at its loss.

She couldn't arouse a modicum of interest in anything. Alex took her out to dinner, a small intimate restaurant where the food was exquisitely excellent, but it could have been sawdust for all she cared. She felt like a wooden doll, lifeless and inarticulate.

With Alex's workload it wasn't difficult to avoid him almost entirely, and apart from a few miserable dinners when he tore himself away from the office, she scarcely saw him at all.

Serafina was sympathetic, if disapproving, believing perhaps that with affection and care, Samantha would eventually regain some of her former wellbeing.

'I need to get away,' Samantha announced starkly over dinner barely three weeks after leaving hospital, and watched as Alex's proud dark head reared back with glittering force.

'Not alone,' he rejected, and she was stung into demanding,

'Why not?'

'Accept that I refuse to let you.'

'I'm not a child,' she cried painfully. 'You can't stop me!'

'I can, very easily.'

Her glance was startlingly eloquent. 'By posting a guard? Serafina and Spiros can't watch me every minute of the day!'

He regarded her steadily. 'Maybe a holiday would be a good idea. Give me time to arrange something.'

'You don't understand. I want to go alone!'

'That's out of the question.'

Her eyes shone with unshed tears. 'I mean to go, Alex.' Her head lifted fractionally, and her voice was remarkably calm. 'With or without your sanction.'

'A trial parting?' he queried silkily. 'What purpose will it serve?'

'I think I want a divorce,' whispered Samantha, sorely tried, and his eyes flared with frightening rage.

'Never.' He seemed almost to devour her, so intensely was she aware of him.

'I can't go on like this,' she managed haltingly, knowing what folly it would be to attempt to explain her feelings.

His eyes hardened until they resembled polished jet, then with a faint sigh he queried, 'Where would you go?'

There was no hesitation. 'Perth. I have friends. I——'

'One week, Samantha,' Alex conceded brusquely. 'The house is empty, and Sophie can go with you.' His dark gaze speared hers mercilessly. 'Don't get any ideas. If you're not on that plane, I'll come and drag you back by your hair. Do you understand?'

'Such tyranny,' she faltered, aghast.

'Call it what you will.'

'I'd rather go alone,' she ventured, suddenly brave in the face of his anger.

'No.'

'I need several weeks. *One* isn't long enough,' she persisted stoically.

'Two weeks, Samantha,' he said hardily, and she raised solemn eyes to his.

'You really intend to let me go?'

His curt indicative nod was the only answer she received.

After that it was only a matter of days before the arrangements were made.

Once it was agreed she could go, it appeared as if Alex was anxious to be rid of her. She saw even less of him, for he was gone before she came down to breakfast, and often sent a message via Serafina that he was working late at the office, or entertaining a business colleague over dinner.

Samantha reflected sadly he didn't even care that whole days went by without catching sight of her, and as for those extended business meetings and dinners—doubtless Rebecca was revelling in them!

The day approached when she was to leave, and she was careful to pack essentials and casual attire. All her glamorous gowns were left on hangers inside the capacious wardrobes, as was the collection of designer shoes and evening bags.

Her scheduled flight was an early morning one,

and Spiros was to collect Sophie en route to the airport. Alex, it appeared, was unable to cancel an important appointment.

At eight she placed a compact and lipstick into her slim make-up purse and thrust it into her shoulderbag, then she cast one slow encompassing glance round the room before emerging into the hall.

A strange hollow feeling manifested itself inside her stomach as she moved down the stairs. Her suitcase had been carried out to the waiting car, and all that remained was to bid Alex goodbye.

Slowly she turned towards the study, as reluctant to enter that room as she was to bypass it.

With a sense of fatalism she tapped her knuckles against the solid panelling, then turned the knob before she had the opportunity to reconsider.

He was standing behind the desk, intent on selecting papers to be placed into an open briefcase, and he looked up as she paused a few feet distant.

Quite what she expected she had no idea. Sarcasm, perhaps; even anger. Not this unnerving silence that made speech almost an impossibility.

'I'd like to thank you,' Samantha ventured at last, and saw one eyebrow lift in cynical query.

'For what, specifically?'

She made an indecisive gesture with her hand, then let it fall back to her side. 'Letting me go,' she said quietly, and was unable to prevent the slight hunger in her gaze as she took her fill of him.

The silence was enervating, and tension seemed to build with each passing second.

'What do you want, Samantha?' Alex demanded softly as he snapped the catches on his briefcase, then closed and locked the desk drawer. 'My blessing?'

He seemed impatient for her to be gone, his mind already occupied with the day's appointments, and she stood hesitantly uncertain as he crossed towards the door.

Would he kiss her? Suddenly she wanted him to, but he displayed not the slightest inclination, and she felt strangely bereft as she preceded him from the room.

Spiros was seated behind the wheel of the Jaguar, and he slid out and opened the passenger door as she walked towards him.

Alex was beside her, and as soon as she was seated he lifted his hand in a brief salute, then strode to the Mercedes parked close behind.

Seconds later Spiros slipped behind the wheel, fired the engine, then eased the large car towards the main gates.

Samantha was conscious of Alex following them, and once clear of the gates she fully expected to see the Mercedes surge past, but it wasn't until Spiros took the expressway leading to the Harbour bridge that Alex shifted to a city-bound lane and within seconds the sports coupé was lost in a sea of traffic.

Sophie was ready and waiting, and Samantha tried to summon enthusiasm for their supposed holiday as they neared the airport.

An incredible lethargy seemed to have crept into her bones, and she mentally shook herself in an effort to dispel it, assuring that this was what she wanted, what she *needed*. What was the matter with her, for heaven's sake? It would be great to spend time at the house, see friends again, be free. Why suffer from second thoughts?

Spiros brought the vehicle to a halt in the car

park, then extracted their bags and escorted them to the passenger terminal.

The walk to the luggage check-in was one of the longest walks she had ever taken, each step bringing her closer to the moment she would depart. Not only out of Sydney, but away from Alex.

She had fought so hard to get away, she couldn't possibly want to stay! Could she? Oh God, she must be going mad!

Spiros took over the machinations of checking in their bags, presenting tickets for seat allocation, then he escorted them to the appropriate lounge on the upper floor.

There was a ten-minute wait until their flight was called, and Samantha lingered, waiting until the majority of passengers had eased through the gate.

'Goodbye, Spiros.' Impulsively she leant forward and brushed her lips to his cheek. 'Look after Alex for me.' The words had come out of their own accord, and her mouth shook a little as she realised what she had said. She drew back, conscious that she and Sophie were the only passengers remaining. 'We must go,' she murmured shakily, and with a faint smile she followed Sophie, not daring to glance back.

The flight was smooth and totally uneventful, and it was a relief to disembark, if only to stretch their legs after so many hours in the air.

Somehow she expected the house to be exactly the same, and although everything looked precisely as they had left it, there was a strange emptiness present.

Someone had been in and dusted, for there wasn't a speck in evidence, and there was food in the refrigerator, the cupboards filled with essentials.

'I'll unpack,' declared Samantha, trying to instil some enthusiasm, and Sophie picked up her bag, indicating she would do likewise.

Afterwards Samantha wandered through the house, touching familiar items of furniture, pausing to straighten a picture frame or shift a vase as she moved from room to room.

The lawns were mown, the garden borders neatly trimmed, without a weed in sight. Even the swing hanging beneath the pepper tree was still there, and she crossed and sat on its wooden seat, moving her feet so the ropes swung gently back and forth.

It was almost four months since she had left, but it could have been that many years. She wanted to feel the same as she had then, to be a carefree, uncomplicated student, sure of the pattern her life would take.

Suddenly restless, she stood to her feet and moved indoors, crossing to the phone. An hour later she had arranged to meet no fewer than three friends for dinner on three consecutive evenings, accepted an invitation to a barbecue the following day, and planned a shopping spree for Monday.

Some of her former *joie de vivre* returned, and that night she slept dreamlessly to wake the next morning feeling refreshed and at ease.

The first week was filled with outings, and the pleasure of being reunited with friends, visiting familiar haunts, held a strange poignancy, and it wasn't until the middle of the following week she began to realise that trying to recapture the past was proving a lost illusion.

Her life had changed, *she* had changed, she reflected sadly. This house was not her home, and she no longer belonged here.

Alex had rung once, but Sophie took the call,

and Samantha declined to speak, indicating silently for Sophie to relay her absence from the house.

Now his image seemed to haunt her, creeping insidiously into her brain until he was all she thought about. The nights were the worst, for then she lay awake remembering how it felt to be in his arms, the tactile sensuality of his touch, and a slow burning ache began in the pit of her stomach—consuming, all-encompassing, unbearable. It was like a deep unassailable hunger demanding fulfilment.

Lust, she reassured herself countless times through those seemingly endless dark hours when the nights seemed so lonely, so empty, she almost screamed at her own folly in putting so much distance between them. Were lust and love interwoven with each other? She was too confused to even think any more.

If it wasn't love, she reflected dazedly as she boarded the jet two days later travelling east, it was a very good imitation. For the first time in weeks she smiled, really smiled, and its effect was dazzling. She felt lightheaded, lighthearted, *happy*. A glow seemed to radiate from deep within, spreading through her body so that she seemed vitally alive.

It was there when she emerged from the plane and stepped into the passenger lounge, her eyes impatient as they skimmed the heads of waiting friends and lovers, searching for the one familiar face she most wanted to see.

Perhaps he was late, or the plane early. In her own mind she couldn't conceive that Alex wouldn't come to meet her. Then she saw Spiros, and it didn't take long to realise he was alone.

A heavy weight seemed to settle round the

region of her heart, and it took considerable effort to appear normal as Spiros deposited Sophie at Manly, then headed back across the harbour towards Point Piper.

Why did she have to suffer such a conflict of emotions? Oh, damn Alex, she cursed helplessly. If he had been at the airport she couldn't have stopped herself from flying straight into his arms. Now she couldn't even *think* clearly.

The Jaguar drew to a halt outside the main entrance, and just as Samantha was about to step out from the car there was a sound of tyres on the metalled driveway behind her.

One glance was sufficient for the nerves in her stomach to begin an agonising somersault, and she stood in mesmerised silence as the Mercedes drew to a halt and Alex emerged from behind the wheel.

Everything she wanted to say remained locked in her throat, and she simply stood there as he walked towards her.

'Welcome home.'

The sound of his voice sent goosebumps scudding every which way in total confusion, and she drew a deep calming breath. 'Hello, Alex.'

His expression was unfathomable as he drew close, and he caught hold of her hand, his fingers threading themselves between hers, but he made no effort to kiss her. 'Did you have a good flight?'

'Yes, thank you.' She sounded incredibly polite, and she missed the faint sharpening of his features as he led her indoors.

'Would you like a drink before freshening up?'

She hesitated fractionally, then gave a nod of acquiescence. Alcohol in one form or another might boost her courage. Heaven knew she needed something to steady the nerves fluttering wildly inside her stomach!

Alex crossed to the drinks cabinet, poured a strong measure of whisky for himself, then mixed a vermouth cocktail, and moved across to where she stood.

'Thank you.' Oh hell, she was beginning to sound like a parrot!

'I presume you enjoyed your holiday,' he drawled. 'You were never home when I rang.'

Samantha took a tentative sip from her glass, then answered civilly, 'I had several friends to see.'

'One imagines you slipped easily back into a familiar routine?'

'Most of my friends were busy attending lectures during the day, except for the weekend.' She lifted her head and met his intent gaze. 'Sophie and I did a fair bit of shopping.'

'And in the evenings you went out.'

If she didn't know better, she could almost imagine he might be jealous. But to even entertain such a thought was crazy—wasn't it? Suddenly reckless, she taunted, 'Every night. Wild parties that lasted until dawn.'

Dark eyes hardened with frightening anger, and his voice was as smooth as silk. 'If I thought that, I'd break every bone in your delectable body.'

Samantha closed her eyes against the compelling sight of him, then slowly opened them again. 'Why not? You've broken everything else.'

There was a measurable silence, then he replaced his glass down on to a nearby table and moved towards her. 'That's a loaded statement— one I'm inclined to make you explain.'

'Oh?' Her eyes became brilliant with a deep inner rage for which there seemed no one particular reason. 'I don't imagine you've sat languishing at home during my absence.' There seemed no stopping her now she'd got started. 'I'm sure Rebecca managed to invent any number of excuses for you to stay late at the office. Then there's always the glamorous Lana to fall back on. Those are two I know about,' she snapped waspishly. 'God knows how many more there are.'

'Rebecca is a very efficient secretary,' Alex drawled. 'But that's all.'

'She doesn't think so!'

'Lana was one of several women—friends, who found it difficult to give up an association which had long been dead.'

Samantha's eyes flashed. 'You mean you used her, as you use me.'

His expression hardened, and his voice became a deep taunting drawl. 'Ah, but you I married, did I not?'

'Oh yes,' she agreed bitterly. 'I live in luxury, waited on hand and foot, my only requirement being to mother your son. Except I failed, didn't I?' To her utter consternation she felt the prick of tears behind her eyes, and she turned and fled, intent on getting out of this room and away from him before she burst into stupid ignominious tears.

Except that she didn't get very far before strong hands caught and held her, then lifted her struggling wildly over one shoulder.

'Put me down, you fiend!' She beat her fists against his back with little effect. *Bastard!*' The tears were streaming from her eyes, running sideways across her temples to become lost in her hair. 'I hate you!'

All the way up the stairs she berated him, and didn't stop when he entered their bedroom. Even the faintly ominous sound of the door being kicked shut did little to halt the venomous flow of words that poured from her mouth.

'Let me go, damn you!'

Without a word he let her slide to the floor, holding her flailing hands without any effort at all.

'Let go my hands!'

He released them, and the instant they were free she lashed out at him, hitting his chest, anywhere she could connect, then he caught them again, holding them in a relentless grip.

'That's enough,' he grated.

Her breathing was ragged, her eyes stormy as she glared at him. 'You always win, don't you?' she demanded bitterly.

'Not always.'

'I don't believe you. You're invincible.'

His expression assumed wry cynicism. 'Appearances can be deceptive.'

Her eyes seemed riveted to his, and her heart almost skipped a beat as a faint glimmer of hope took root. 'Why do we always fight?' she whispered shakily.

'I had hoped you might have figured it out by now.'

Maybe, just maybe she had. She stood hesitant and silent, her eyes begging him to give some indication, but he chose to ignore her plea.

'You haven't lacked the ability to speak your mind in the past,' said Alex. 'Why be afraid now?'

Before I wasn't afraid of losing you, she cried silently, unsure how to proceed, or even if she should. After a long silence she ventured slowly, 'I thought everything I wanted was back in Perth.'

'And it isn't?'

The air between them seemed suddenly charged with latent emotion, and her heart gave a lurch as she saw a muscle tense along his jaw.

'No.'

'What changed your mind?'

Her chin lifted, and her eyes were remarkably

clear as they met his. 'You,' she said simply. 'It was almost as if I'd been working on a giant jigsaw, and suddenly the last few pieces fell into place.' Tears pricked the back of her eyes. 'You should never have let me go.'

Alex didn't say a word, and a faint feeling of fear shivered its way down the length of her spine.

'I wanted to hate you for forcing me into marriage,' she continued bravely. 'And at first I did. I don't know when it began to change. Maybe when you were in hospital. I resented Rebecca,' she owned shakily, giving a rueful half-smile, 'Lana, and any woman who even looked at you. Then when I became pregnant, it seemed as if I'd become so much a part of you that in doing so I lost my own identity. After I miscarried, I became even more confused.' She took a deep breath, then released it with an anguished cry. 'You want it all, don't you? *I love you*. What more do you want? That I should beg?'

'Would you?'

'Do I have to?' She was dangerously close to tears, and she hurt all over. Why did love have to involve so much *pain*?

A hand reached for her chin, lifting it with strong fingers so that she had little choice but to look at him.

'I think you should show me some of this love you're talking about,' Alex drawled softly, and there was still an inflexible quality evident in those tautly chiselled features.

'Why?' Samantha beseeched. 'So you can throw it back in my face?'

'Is that what you think?'

She looked at him in silence, her pale face almost white. He was so close, yet so far away. One more step, and she would be in his arms. Yet that distance represented so much. If he rejected her, she might as well curl up and die.

Slowly she moved forward, lifting her arms to encircle his neck, and her hands linked together, urging his head down to hers.

Her mouth sought his, her lips soft and generous as they made an initial tentative exploration.

'I love you. Long before you deserved to be loved.' The hauntingly vulnerable words whispered into his mouth, poignant and achingly sincere, and a long shuddering sigh shook through his powerful body as he gathered her close.

Then his mouth possessed hers with a hunger that left no room for doubt, and she exulted in the strength of his arms, the force of his arousal, as he kissed her until she could hardly breathe.

Gently he relinquished her lips and bent to savour the rapidly beating pulse at the base of her throat, before moving down the vee of her blouse, his fingers seeking the buttons and undoing several to reveal the sensitised flesh of her breasts.

With unhurried movements he dispensed with her bra, then slowly sought first one taut peak before trailing gently to render a similar supplication to its twin.

The barrier his shirt represented was easily removed, and her fingers were brazen in their exploration as they caressed with tactile intimacy.

'Witch,' Alex groaned with a faintly derisive smile. 'Look what you've done to me!'

'I think the feeling is mutual,' Samantha murmured huskily, feeling a slow tide of colour creep over her body as she bore his appraisal.

His eyes became soft and slumbrous with passion. 'What do you suppose we should do about it?'

She pretended to consider, tilting her head to one side, a tiny smile widening her lips. 'I have an idea or two '

Alex released a husky growl. 'Have you, indeed?'

The delight in teasing him brought a devilish twinkle to her eyes. 'After dinner?'

'Are you saying you're *hungry*?'

'Well, I guess I will be, eventually.' A delicious laugh bubbled up from her throat, and her eyes held a provocative gleam. 'Aren't you going to kiss me?'

A finger traced the length of her nose, then slid over its tip to tease the outline of her mouth.

'Are you proposing I make love to you?'

'I hope so,' she owned tremulously. 'I ache so much with wanting, *needing*, you.'

His hands were gentle as they sought her waist, then he swung her into his arms and carried her towards the bed. He paused only long enough to remove the remainder of her clothes, then he discarded his own.

Samantha linked her hands behind his head, then she kissed him, gently at first, glorying in taking the initiative until Alex took over, and there was a pertinent hunger in his touch, a vulnerability she had not expected, so that she drew back, gently staying that wandering mouth.

'Alex——'

At the slight doubt in her eyes his hands reached out and framed her face, his gaze steady as it met hers, and his lips softened.

'I married you with one thought in mind,' he admitted carefully. 'Payment in human form. A wife had several advantages, and I intended to make full use of them.' The edge of his mouth twisted slightly with wry self-derision. 'You crept beneath my skin, and once you were there, I was unable to dislodge you. After a while, I didn't want to. As to whether it might be *love*——' he paused fractionally, 'I hadn't believed in it up until then, and saw no reason to start. Being hospitalised gave me time to evaluate the fierce anger I felt every time I saw George anywhere near you.' He gave a wry grimace, and his eyes darkened measurably. 'You seemed so natural with him, so unaffected, and seeing you together only brought the realisation that the emotion I experienced was jealousy. With typical male arrogance, I thought I could utilise persuasion to make you love me. In bed we were physically in accord, but out of it we tended to rage at each other like opponents on a battlefield.' His eyes kindled with deep regret as his hands made a gentle soothing movement up and down her spine. One hand lifted to cup her face, while the other trailed softly over its contours with gentle reverence.

'I am so much older than you,' Alex allowed with regret. 'While not exactly a rake, I can't deny there have been many women.' His voice was tinged with rueful resignation.

'You're only thirty-seven,' she protested, and he shook his head.

'Seventeen years, my sweet Samantha. When you're fifty, I'll be nearing seventy.'

Her eyes were wide and luminous as she gazed at his endearingly familiar features. 'That's more than thirty years away,' she said shakily. 'How can anyone know what will happen in the future?' Her eyes filled with tears. 'I love you, Alex Nicolaos, with all my heart. Are you saying we shouldn't have those years together just because when you're almost in your dotage I'll only be on the down side of middle age?' Her voice became filled with

genuine anger. 'Do you honestly think my love is
so shallow I won't *grow* with you, accept the subtle
changes *because* I love you?' She felt as if she was
on fire, so intense was her indignation. 'If you're
willing to throw it away, then——'

His mouth closed over hers, hard and posses-
sively demanding as he sought to wipe out her
uncertainty and pain, staking a lifetime claim he
had no intention of relinquishing.

'You are my love—my life,' Alex vowed huskily.

Then he made love to her, gently and with such
reverence that she actually cried, and he kissed the
tears from her lashes before tasting every inch of
her face.

It was an intensely evocative sensation that
brought alive every sensory nerve-ending, until her
whole body seemed to throb with awareness.

Not content, he nuzzled the soft hollows at the
base of her throat before moving lower to savour
the hardening peak of each breast, and she gave a
moan of entreaty as he trailed his lips across the
flatness of her stomach and began a slow
downward path that had her sobbing for release
from the swirling molten vortex of emotion.

It was a long time before he lifted her high into
his arms and carried her to the bathroom, where
he filled the capacious tub before gently lowering
her into it, then he stepped in and turned on the
spa jets.

The softly surging action of the water was
soothing, and Samantha felt incredibly warm and
at peace, secure in the afterglow of lovemaking.

Alex's gaze was incredibly intimate, and her eyes
seemed to melt, their golden depths sparkling with
inner contentment.

'No regrets?'

A soft smile curved her lips as she shook her

head. 'How could I have any?'

There was a faint buzz as the intercom signalled its existence, and Spiros' voice came through the speaker.

'Will you be requiring dinner this evening? If not, Serafina will put everything away.'

Samantha's eyes blazed with hidden laughter, and she stepped out of the tub, crossing to depress the intercom button. 'What time is it, Spiros?'

'Nine o'clock.'

A glance towards her husband revealed that his attention was centred on the gleaming contours of her slim curves, and she wrinkled her nose at him before issuing instructions. 'Tell Serafina we'll be down in fifteen minutes.'

Collecting a towel, she wound it sarong-wise round her body, ignoring Alex's silent beckoning gesture to rejoin him.

'Out, you insatiable man,' she commanded teasingly. *'Food!'* She bent and bunched his towel and threw it towards him.

'I'd much prefer to stay here,' Alex murmured quizzically, and she laughed with husky enjoyment.

'If I know Serafina, she will have taken pride in setting a very romantic table with candles and a fine wine to toast our reunion.' Her eyes slid over his tautly muscled frame with a warm hunger. 'It would be a shame not to indulge her, don't you think?'

'Oh, definitely a shame,' he taunted with devilish cynicism, and Samantha tore her eyes away as he stood to his feet.

'I'm going to get dressed,' she said unsteadily, turning towards the bedroom.

She chose clothes at random, slipping into a tailored skirt and blouse, then she tugged a brush through her hair and applied a soft colour to her lips.

As she straightened from the mirror Alex moved to stand within touching distance, and she almost melted at the warmth of his gaze as he bent his head to caress the exposed hollow at the base of her neck.

'Alex——'

'Shh!' he chastised gently, turning her round to face him. 'Just a kiss, nothing more, hmm?'

It was a tender gesture, his lips making gentle forays over the softness of her mouth, then he reluctantly moved back a pace and caught hold of her hand. 'Coming?'

She looked at him in silence, then said quietly, 'Anywhere you choose to lead. For the rest of my life.'

'Amen to that,' Alex husked gently, pulling her close to his side, and together they walked from the room.

ROMANCE

Variety is the spice of romance

Each month, Mills & Boon publish new romances. New stories about people falling in love. A world of variety in romance — from the best writers in the romantic world. Choose from these titles in October.

DARKER SIDE OF DESIRE Penny Jordan
UNTAMED Carole Mortimer
THE OPEN MARRIAGE Flora Kidd
BORN OF THE WIND Margaret Pargeter
DARK TYRANT Helen Bianchin
LINGERING EMBERS Lynsey Stevens
AN INDEPENDENT WOMAN Claire Harrison
THE FRENCHMAN'S KISS Claudia Jameson
CAPE OF MISFORTUNE Yvonne Whittal
INTIMATE Donna Huxley
THE EGO TRAP Elizabeth Oldfield
FIRE OF THE GODS Madeleine Ker

On sale where you buy paperbacks. If you require further information or have any difficulty obtaining them, write to: Mills & Boon Reader Service, PO Box 236, Thornton Road, Croydon, Surrey CR9 3RU, England.

Mills & Boon
the rose of romance

 **ROMANCE**

Next month's romances from Mills & Boon

Each month, you can choose from a world of variety in romance with Mills & Boon. These are the new titles to look out for next month.

RULES OF THE GAME Penny Jordan
AN UNWILLING DESIRE Carole Mortimer
FACADE Jessica Steele
A TIME TO GROW Claudia Jameson
LOVE'S TANGLED WEB Mary Lyons
ISLAND OF DOLPHINS Lilian Cheatham
OUT OF THIS DARKNESS Madeleine Ker
FLASHBACK Amanda Carpenter
PERSONAL VENDETTA Margaret Mayo
FALLEN IDOL Margaret Way
MEGAN'S FOLLY Maura McGiveny
NUMBER ONE Donna Huxley

Buy them from your usual paperback stockist, or write to: Mills & Boon Reader Service, P.O. Box 236, Thornton Rd, Croydon, Surrey CR9 3RU, England. Readers in South Africa-write to: Mills & Boon Reader Service of Southern Africa, Private Bag X3010, Randburg, 2125.

Mills & Boon
the rose of romance